six simpletruths™
to Fat Release

Available to You from the Author

Log on to www.SixSimpleTruths.com
to learn more about:

Live tele-workshop coaching

Free guided visualization audio

Free affirmations audio

Updated inspirational blog articles

Free downloads

Inspirational before and after photos

Free upcoming events to participate in

Valuable resources and tools for
your transformation

Join us in our supportive community
of people helping people.

Be sure to mail in the postcard in back
of this book for more information.

six simple truths™
to Fat Release

How I Let Go of More Than 100 Pounds the Easy Way

by Nealon Hightower

mPOWER PRESS

*I **can** tell you it worked for me. – Nealon*

Published in the United States by mPower Press

For more information about special discounts for bulk purchases please contact: www.mPowerpress.com, Atlanta, GA

Editing by Emily Hope Avent
Cover design by Marcia Lampe
Photos by Kelly Hightower

ISBN 978-1-935636-98-4

For you, Dad,
This book is dedicated to the loving memory of my father,
Frederick A. Hightower, Jr.

Without your love, encouragement, and support, none of this would
have come about in the beautiful way that it has. Thank you for all
the gifts you gave me, and most of all, thank you for believing in me
even when I didn't know how to believe in myself.
I still feel your love in my heart, Dad, every day.

For those who know the struggle,
I have found a path that can work for you. Know that you have been
in my heart from the very beginning. You can do this!

My Vision

"My vision is to help people create an environment
where a satisfied mind can prevail; where the pain and
sickness of obesity are replaced with joy and passion
so they too can freely give the world their special and
unique gifts and through such action enable a global
shift in consciousness thereby bringing light where
there previously was darkness."

CONTENTS

"When the remedy you have offered only increases the disease, then leave him who will not be cured, and tell your story to someone who seeks the truth." — *Rumi*

INTRODUCTION

HOPE IS ALIVE and pulsing within us all. I am here to tell a story of courage, of faith, of allowing, and most of all, of love. My journey through life seemed long and hard. My struggles seemed so trying at times, but it is all very clear to me now why it had to be. It all was and is good, right, and perfect.

I was overweight as a young child. It brings with it a familiar pain that I still feel at times today as an adult when these old thoughts are triggered. I know the feeling of not belonging, of not being normal, of not looking like and feeling like everyone else. I managed to adapt, as we all do in life, and I managed to cope with the cards I had been given, even using them to my advantage at times but never seeming to get the fulfillment I was in an endless search for. Fulfillment eluded me regardless of the temporary successes that frequently came my way. I always had a knowing deep within my heart that there just had to be another way. Surely I was not put on this planet, or had not chosen this life, to suffer. Surely there had to be a better way, a better plan, something else that would just feel right!

This is the story of how I found that peace. I've unraveled what I did, went back and looked at it, and now I am showing you what transpired that you may find your way, too. Sometimes all we need is a little help to point us in the right direction, like a lost traveler in a strange land. Think of me as a friendly face on your path pointing you to shelter and comfort. There is no longer a need to feel lost.

Please know, wherever you may be, whatever your situation, there is hope. There is always hope. Even if your challenge is not even one of being overweight, please stop for a moment and get this. As long as there's breath in your lungs and warm blood in your veins, there is hope. I've since seen so many magical things happen. I've witnessed beautiful things happen to even more beautiful people because they held their hands out to hope. Please believe and trust me when I say that you have the strength of the entire universe inside you, right now. You are a beautiful manifestation of a perfect world in perfect balanced order. I now know that there are no "coincidences," as we call them. The events in your life are perfect, although you may not yet have figured out how or why yet. You don't have to all at once. It will all be clear to you once you begin to step into the light.

The ideas I lay out here are simple. You may or may not allow them to come easily at first, which will be up to you, but I encourage you to do your best to stay out of your own way and allow this to be as easy as it is and can be. The truth is simple; by nature, it is easy. The universe struggles with nothing; only humans do, and we don't have to.

We all know people who have touched our lives in one way or another somewhere along the line. I have been fortunate enough to have more than a couple. One was a high school history teacher by the name of Mr. James Littlefield. He once walked up to the chalkboard, drew a pie chart, and said, "There are things in this world that we know we know." This

2

took up a small piece of the pie. He continued, "Then there are the things we know we don't know." That took up a considerably larger piece of the chart. He finished, "And then there are the things we don't know we don't know." That took up the vast majority of the pie.

You see, we know so little compared to what there is to know. I ask you to keep an open mind and suggest that some of the ideas here may actually fall in that last category. They are simple, greatly evidenced, and life changing.

One of the things you may not know is that becoming healthy can be easy. Forget whatever else you may think you know in regards to how hard it will be. Don't be misled by your ego, which may try to convince you that it can't be this easy. It has struggled with these problems your entire life. It has taken credit for every success and justified every failure. Its existence depends on your resistance to these simple truths. So, be aware of that little person and willingly surrender this ego; let your heart fully absorb what is laid down before you. The information contained can do no harm, only good. It's based on your true nature. It is in you already. It should have a familiar ring to your soul like a song you know you've heard before.

You are close, maybe closer than you've ever been. There may be times when you find yourself putting this book down and not picking it back up, even though it was all going so smoothly and well. This is just fear in disguise. There is nothing to be afraid of. Fear is one of the many things you will learn to let go of here on this journey. So, if you encounter this fear, it's perfectly normal; just be aware of its presence, allow it to be present, and calmly flow around it like water around a smooth stone in a brook.

I've never been, and I'm not now, one to close my eyes and pretend that our problems don't exist. If they didn't, we wouldn't be looking for solutions. Problems are real. They need to be acknowledged and cared for. Like my good friend Dr. Sharon Lamm-Hartman teaches, new trust statements must be built in place of them. Remember, these fears and other challenges you may encounter are the fabric for the canvas on which you're going to paint your perfect life. Celebrate them. Learn from them. Grow from them. Allow them to exist, and realize that in reality, life's hardest challenges actually become our greatest gift to give the world. It is through that hardship, which we triumph over, that we truly become able to teach others, and by doing so, help them to more fully enjoy life.

Until you've walked a mile in another's shoes, everything else is just theory. Though I wrote this book coming from a place of being morbidly obese, I have experienced that and everything in between. I know that no matter where you fall on that spectrum, what I've outlined here is the universal truth. It can help. It will help if only you allow.

"All truths are easy to understand once they are discovered; the point is to discover them." — *Galileo Galilei*

SIX SIMPLE TRUTHS

• • • • • •

AUTHOR'S NOTE

I ORIGINALLY RESISTED putting any of my personal story in this book. I really wanted to hold on to my privacy, and I wasn't sure I wanted to share that much with a world of strangers. In the end, I asked my heart what to do and it gave me a definite and resounding answer: "Yes! Put it in!"

You are not a stranger to me. We are more alike than you may know. I want to establish a platform of trust with you. I want you to know, before we begin, that my single and only expectation is for you to succeed in this endeavor, if that is your intention. I see you as healed already; I can see you in no other way. I've felt your pain in the past, but now I only see the happiness and joy that you will come to experience. Align your intentions, and your success becomes not only possible, but inevitable. There can be no other possible outcome. Only a period of time, mostly dependent on you, lies between you and that which you desire, your perfect health. You will have your health, but the unexpected treasures that come along with it will far overshadow even your new, fit body. You will come to know this, and when you do, please let me know. I live for this.

So thank you for trusting me, even if just a little, and allowing me into the sacred part of your soul that has so few visitors.

I know that place. I know it can be difficult to trust and to try again, but I ask you to allow yourself to believe that this will work out and to expect to get the results you so dearly desire, even if you have to hold these beliefs very deep within you and not share them with anyone. That's OK. Do whatever you need to do to put that one foot out there. I didn't tell a soul I was attempting weight loss until I was well under way. To be honest, I think it was because I was so unsure I'd be able to do it, and I didn't want to let anyone else down or appear like an even bigger failure to my children and wife and friends. My point is that this was OK. This is between you and your heart. You have everything you'll need to begin this journey. You've always had it. You came complete into this world. You came whole. You still are.

So where do we begin? Yes, the age old question that has been pondered so long by so many and been the cause of so much delay and postponement in many an endeavor. This may seem as fantastic an effort as you've fancied in a while, so to quote a wonderful story of fantasy and dream, as the King said to White Rabbit, "Begin at the beginning." There's a whole other world just waiting for you. Let's go. It's time.

"Truth will ultimately prevail where there is pains to bring it to light." — *George Washington*

SIX SIMPLE TRUTHS
● ● ● ● ● ●

· · · · · ·

MY STORY

"THIS IS GOING to be too hard."

"Well, Nealon, what if it were easy?"

"Huh?"

"What if it were easy?"

And that's when I saw the first glimmer of light in my life in a very long time.

"Easy? How do you mean?"

I felt knocked out, on the mat, down for the count, and my inner wisdom was extending a loving hand, as if to say gently and quietly, "Get up. We can do this."

I slowly got up, a little mistrustful, a lot hurt, and I listened as the part of me that still had some strength continued to speak, gently, softly, but with a reassuring conviction in its tone that made me curious enough to continue to listen.

"What if it were easy, Neal? If it were easy, could you? Would you? Tell *me* what it would look like if it were easy."

This was the very real dialogue that took place within me on a fateful day some time ago. I'll never forget it. It was the start of something beautiful and the end of something more painful than I can now imagine.

· · · · · ·

I've struggled with my weight, and not unlike any other over-weight person, I've tried nearly every diet and program out there, from eating only cabbage soup at age nine to diet shakes at age eleven to just not eating as a teenager. As I grew into an adult and learned about nutrition, I graduated to some more sophisticated diets, but always with the same end result: I ended up back where I started, usually with a little extra fat as a reward for my efforts. This revolving door never seemed to take me anywhere I wanted to go and left me with such a deep frustration. How could I be good at so many other things in my life but when it came to this, nothing? It just didn't make sense to me. The more I tried to make sense of it, the more confused I became. The harder I tried, the harder I fell. Every time I ended up heavier and heavier, more unhealthy and feeling hopelessly confused. I could take no more.

So at age thirty-one, I gave up. That's right. I quit, threw in the towel, and punched out. I stopped mindlessly ramming my head against the proverbial brick wall. I found a way to accept things the way they were. I justified my weight problem with a variety of clever and believable excuses, ranging from poor genetics (the majority of my family was, after all, overweight, too) to chemicals and pesticides in our bioengineered food that could simply not be avoided. (I mean, it couldn't have been the beer and the chicken wings, right?) I counterbalanced my condition and my new conclusion with a reassuring knowledge that there were many other things I was good at; perhaps that was just the way nature wanted it. I figured with my strengths came my weaknesses, some kind of a yin and yang balance of sorts. "We'll let you succeed here and there, but not over there."

MY STORY

· · · · · ·

I remember many times thinking that if I could only have whipped that weight problem, I would certainly be happy, and as an added bonus I would be able to deal with any other problem that came my way. Nope, this ole boy was just going to stay where he was at. Although I was well over 300 lbs, my weight didn't seem to be climbing out of control at the moment, so maybe this was just the natural weight for me. Perhaps this was what my weight was supposed to be. I must have been some kind of genetic anomaly, a freak of sorts, and this was my intended weight. It was awful, but like I said, I was finished, no more, all done with this game. I'm a fighter, but I know when I'm beat. This should have been the end of the story…but it wasn't.

By this point I was the father of a beautiful and happy little boy and married to a wife who seemed to embrace my deficiencies so long as I reciprocated. I was living in a beautiful home, in the midst of the worst financial economy that many generations had ever seen. It was the worst housing market I'd ever even read about, and I was in residential construction. My business was failing miserably. I put up the hardest and most brutal battle I'd ever been through to recover the business I had worked so hard to build with my father, and it still fell like a house of cards in a gentle breeze. That was a blow. It seemed, from my perspective at the time, that everything I had worked so hard to build was effortlessly being taken away, and there was absolutely nothing I could do about it.

Now I was in a quandary, even more confused than before. I mean, I had always, at the very least, had financial success, which I could point to to justify the imbalance of the other lacking areas of my life, namely my health. I had been a successful entrepreneur from a very young age. No matter that it was my thing; the cards were certainly stacked against a speculative homebuilder in late 2007. I fought with everything I had to keep it alive. I stayed up at night, literally in tears because I couldn't repay the good folks who had trusted me with loans and obligations. I had my ass handed to me, as they say. I was downright beat to a pulp with nothing more to turn to but food and drink. This was just too painful to watch in real life, so I numbed out with food, alcohol, sleep, whatever would make it feel better for the moment, and my weight went up and up and up. I stopped weighing myself. I didn't want to know.

The doctor said I had something called fatty liver disease. Apparently, there was just too much fat around my organs, especially in and around my liver. My good doctor sent me to a specialist, who suggested I get some exercise and try to lose some weight. That was it. *Get some exercise and try to lose some weight?* I have to admit, the only thing that would temporarily pause my deep sense of depression was my feeling of anger when I heard something like this coming from my very own doctor. "Try to lose some weight? Are you kidding me? Don't you think I've thought of that? Don't you think I've tried that more times than I care to count? Is that the best you've got for me?"

My health problems, as you may imagine, did not end there. I had long suspected I had sleep apnea, a condition where you never really get a full night's sleep because the weight of your own torso crushes your air passageway. Snoring gets very loud and disruptive, and I would have bouts of not breathing for thirty to sixty seconds or more, only to have my body abruptly awaken to prevent suffocation. I could never hit the deeper levels of sleep that were necessary to feel truly rested the next day. This was every night, no exceptions, for years on end every time I slept. My poor wife. This put me in a constant state of exhaustion and depleted my energy—whatever little I had been able to muster—compounded by the fact that I was carrying around the equivalent of another human being on my frame. I was damn tired and hungover 30 percent of the time, to boot. The black-and-white picture on the cover tells the story better than I can. If you cover up the "after" shot and look deep into my face, you can feel my pain. It's just below the surface. Photos like this of me crashed out on the couch were not uncommon. I was tired. I was beat.

It was around this time that my beautiful Henry was born. So here I was father of two great sons with a wife who was scared and couldn't understand why there was no money coming in, wondering how we were going to support our growing family, probably starting to wonder if she was with the right person.

I had an expensive and beautiful big four-wheel-drive truck squeezed into the garage that needed to be sold before it was taken away. I loved that truck. I was putting a finishing coat of wax on it in the garage around midnight, probably seven or eight beers deep. The phone rang. A friend needed to be picked up about an hour away from home. I grabbed Jojo, our little pug, threw her in my truck, and headed down the highway, probably faster than I should have been going.

OK, this part hurts, so I'll move quickly. I was pulled over and failed a field sobriety test. The truck and dog were impounded, and I was sent to county jail to think this over. Now, I hope you've never had the honor of spending the night in one of these fine establishments, but in all honesty, it wasn't my first time. Plainly put, it sucks. I'm sorry, but there's isn't another way to correctly put it. All I kept thinking was that I was better than this, but here I was. I've always been a big believer in taking personal responsibility, so there was no dodging this one. I was in worse shape than a bad country song, dog and all.

My wife was at home with our three-week-old and our two-year-old. I know the only reason she even got out of bed that night and put the nursing infant in his second car ride ever was because of the dog. I couldn't say I blamed her. I think I'd have just left me there. At least in there, no one expected much of me. Just move to the next room where they record some more information and throw you a dry bologna sandwich. If you're lucky you get a mustard packet.

I must say, that's about the worst I've ever felt about myself. Broke, jailed, depressed, and fat, to top it all off. I trudged along and once again hopelessly revisited the idea of losing weight, but how could I? I certainly felt like a failure in almost every way a man could be. Sooner or later I'd *always* failed on diets in the past, 100 percent of the time, and I usually felt pretty darn good when I started them. Right now, I felt awful. I didn't want to get out of bed, much less go to the gym. How could this feeble attempt at my weakened state possibly succeed?

I guess there's something in the human spirit that allows you to go just a little further, even when you're sure you can't, because somehow, I picked myself up one more time and said, "OK. I'll consider trying again. What do you want me to do?"

An inner dialogue took place that cold, wet November morning, which I'll never forget until the day I die. A quiet but concerned and determined voice was speaking to me, telling me that I was leaving too much on the table and not fully engaging in my life.

This voice was right. I had always convinced myself that I would always do a better job than my parents and not let my children go through the same pain that I went through as an obese child. Here I was setting a much worse example for my children than my parents had ever done and preparing to leave them early to figure it out on their own. I'm sure it was so obvious to everyone else, but I was oblivious until this moment.

I wiped the tears from my eyes, brushed myself off, and started down a theoretical—no, imaginary, almost make believe—road about what weight loss would be like if it were easy. Slowly, imaginary became real. That is how this book and my current state of affairs came to be.

So I understand the fragile state you may be in. I understand the feeling of hopelessness that runs through so many. The sense of "knowing" that it will never get any better. I know.

But it will get better. There's a way out and it's easy. I figured this out because I promised myself it would have to be easy for it to work, for me to even try. What I didn't realize at the time is that it is not only easy, it's effortless.

You see, the conventional approach to "weight loss" has always been to search for the answer "out there." People spend vast amounts of money hoping to find or buy the answer in a workout video, in a new gym membership, with a personal trainer, in a new diet, in a prepackaged meal, in some kind of surgery, or in yet one more drug or pill. I'm not even suggesting that any of these things, in and of themselves, are bad. Most are not.

The thing is, they just aren't where the true answer is. You see, the truth is free. It always has been. That's one of the great things about it. Another is that it is always inherently simple. Another is that it can be easy.

"Free, simple, and easy? Come on, Nealon, what are you talking about? The fat on your butt must have been made out of something different than the fat on mine."

No, it was the same. Look, we've all "lost weight" before, right? Sure, overweight people are the best dieters in the world. My guess is, we've lost more weight and gained it back than the total weight of the rest of the population combined! (I can't prove that, but I bet you it's not far from the truth.) I know I've lost and gained and lost and gained and lost and gained probably well over one thousand pounds over the years. We have more willpower than most of the world. We've logged more miles on treadmills and hours on exercise equipment than Olympic athletes. We've spent more money trying to lose weight than other folks spend on Christmas and retirement combined in a lifetime. It is *not* for lack of effort!

And this is why it bothers me when some skinny person comes on TV pimping some new product and says, "Just buy this and eat that, and the weight will just fall off in only four weeks for four easy payments of $49.95." Well, let me tell you, the only thing easy about most of these things is how easy the money comes out of your account. Besides, I'd have loved just to look like most of these guys' or gals' "before" pictures, if they even have them.

I'm here to tell you that it can be FREE, SIMPLE, and EASY. You only have to have a belief that it can be so. So let's jump in.

"They can because they think they can." — *Virgil*

"The thing you fear most has no power. Your fear of it is what has the power. Facing the truth really will set you free." — *Oprah Winfrey*

SIX SIMPLE TRUTHS
• • • • • •

• • • • • •

GRATITUDE

Simple Truth 1
A state of gratitude attracts
good into your life.

THE FIRST STEP to attracting better health to ourselves lies in gratitude. This is where, in the past, I've lost control of the horse, right out of the gate, before I ever even hit my stride. We're so used to being surrounded by folks who are constantly complaining about everything from the weather to the economy. We're constantly focusing on what's wrong, not on what's right, or even more importantly, what we *do* want.

It amazes me how people will get so focused on an eight percent unemployment rate. My father was always quick to point out that 92 percent of the population was still working. In any other area of our lives, 92 percent is pretty darn good. It's a whole lot better than some of my old math grades. Or that one-third of the population is obese when a larger two-thirds *majority* is not! That's right, according to Center for Disease Control, in a study of adults in 2007-2008, most of us in the United States are *not* obese, even with all of the bad habits and junk food and chemicals and other obstacles that can get in the way of good health. I'm not suggesting that a 33 percent obesity rate is good or even not that bad, I'm just saying that there are people who live in the same environment, all around us, who face the same elements; and they don't seem to have as intense a problem. Many of them don't even seem to be paying attention to what they're eating. Why?

How do we get to be employed or thin or anything that we really want to be doing better? By submersing ourselves in the company of people who are unemployed or fat or have a lack? Of course not, just the opposite. You see, what we think about we bring about. So much of what we think about, we talk about with the people around us. They influence our thoughts and we influence theirs, and we both have more of the same kinds of thoughts. This is how we've evolved as a species. It's how anything out there is brought from mind to reality.

We all manifest things into reality every single day: our clothes, our jobs, the people around us, our pets, our things, and so on and so on. We make it all appear from our thoughts. My father was known for saying that everything people have ever brought into creation had to be created twice, once in the mind and another in the physical realm. Therefore, if you focus on your current state, you will recreate your current state of affairs over and over, perhaps making it worse, depending on your thoughts and the emotions you fuel them with. Put your attention on being fat, broke, unhappy, you fill in the blank, and you manifest more of those same circumstances. It's counterintuitive to think that you could create something different. Nothing has ever been brought into creation by thinking and focusing on the lack of that very thing. It's by thinking about what it would take to have that thing. It's really not all that mystical, as some people think it is. Let's look at it in slightly different terms that might hit a little closer to home.

You're hungry. It's 1:30 p.m. You've still not eaten lunch. What do you start thinking about? A burger, maybe some pizza? Think about that for about thirty minutes, and when the opportunity presents itself, what happens? Bam! You're eating it! You've probably become very good at that if you've felt the need to buy (or manifest) this book.

So now, let's look at the dynamics of what just happened. First you thought about hunger, even felt the familiar grumblings of it once you dialed in on the thought. Next, you thought about some different food options. Next, you became aware of a joint that could provide one of those things (or something better)—and pop! You took action and came to be eating the thing that was first only in your mind.

What do you think would happen if you didn't think about being hungry? What if you didn't think about a burger or pizza? You may be thinking, "You don't understand. When so much time has passed and it's time for me to eat, those things just automatically pop into my head." Ah, but here's the difference between me and 90 percent of the other people who've written about this subject. I do understand. I've been there.

How do you think you made it to 1:30 p.m. (or later in many cases) in the first place when you normally eat at noon? Simple (and easy), you probably got distracted by something else (kids, work, traffic) and just weren't thinking about it. Your focus was elsewhere. There isn't a built-in clock that determines when you must eat, though you may watch the clock on the wall for cues. Your thoughts bring it about and trigger an action. The kind of food you thought about and focused on is what magically ended up in your mouth. So you can clearly see how your thoughts become things with food, something you can probably relate to all too well.

Here's the thing: it "magically" works with everything in your life. Think about it, focus on it, dwell on it; you might even have visualized it and tasted it in your mind (did you salivate?); you may have even put a little emotional fuel behind it. You could have even affirmed it: "I'm stopping at the first fast food joint I see." All are very powerful tools you employed. All of them you are already very good at. All things we are going to use to your advantage.

You see, you are farther along than you may think. There's nothing new here to change but what you *choose* to focus on. See how this will be effortless? You already know how. It's not like you need to learn a new set of skills.

So where does gratitude come in? Right here. :: enter stage left, gratitude :: If you start with the things you already have that are good in your life, your mind will start to focus on those instead of the things that are not producing the desired result. You will then start to see things that you otherwise would have passed right up, like the opportunity to watch a beautiful sunset, to have a great conversation with a close friend, or the option of a healthy meal that was just as available to you as an unhealthy one.

It doesn't matter how much you have to be grateful for. The universe doesn't care how much or how little you have. It just knows to send you more of whatever you focus on. It works every time if you can stay in that grateful state of mind.

You may be thinking what I was thinking when I first started my journey: "What in the world do I have to be grateful for?" I had just lost my business, my vehicle, and I was in awful shape, tired, and miserable, feeling like I was without hope.

GRATITUDE

· · · · · ·

I could hardly make it up two flights of stairs all at once. My checkbook was empty. I was even in jail at one point, with my freedom being restricted.

You may be in a far worse place than I was; I'm certainly not trying to take that away from you or to compare battle wounds. But, friend, take heart. It doesn't matter. You see, if that is the case, you actually have much more experience than I did to draw on and much more to give back to the world once you've gone through this dark period. You may have traveled to deeper depths than I did, and your story will read differently than mine, and you will be able to speak to people I just can't reach. It's all good and perfect. The only thing you really need to trust here is your own heart. The important thing to remember in the beginning is what you *do* have, not what you do not. So, what do you have?

Like I've said, as long as you're alive, you do have things to be grateful for. You may have children, friends, family, a great job (any job), or you may live in a great area. Perhaps you are fortunate enough to have the use of all your limbs, or maybe you have your eyesight, or perhaps you can hear. You get the idea. You won't have to look far once you become aware and start to actually look for the good. There's always someone who would trade places with you in an instant given the opportunity. Keep that in mind as you're practicing gratitude.

Gratitude is one of the easier truths to put into practice. It requires no money, no trip to the gym; it doesn't even require you to put down that brownie, get off the couch, or turn off the TV. The only thing this simple truth requires you to change is your current level of appreciation for what you already have. See? Easy, right? Stay with me, it gets even better.

This in turn will open you up to receive, as there is a very good chance you are in some way closed off to receiving good right now, at least in as much as your personal health is concerned. As I told you, for most of my life I had most other areas of my life in pretty good shape. It was only when I came face to face with my health issues and financial wreckage that I allowed that real and permanent change to come to me. When we stay in a mindset that is focused on misery and what is not right, we cannot be at the same time open to receive. The good news is when we are truly open to receive, we cannot stay in a mindset that is focused on misery.

This is because we have only two core emotions: fear and love. One feels good. The other does not. Let your feelings be your guide. If you really are open to receive and grateful, you cannot at the same time be afraid or be focusing on lack. You cannot truly stay in both of them at the same time. It really is that simple.

So let's say, for example, you're down in the dumps and feeling awful and want to take the first step. What is it? Remember, I told myself I would only go down this road again if it were easy.

Here is what it looks like. Every morning, when you arise, put your feet on the ground (if you can), walk over to the nearest mirror, stretch out your arms wide, look at yourself with a big smile (force the first one out if you have to), and say,

Today and every day, I am open to receive all of the abundance and beautiful gifts the universe has for me!

Follow this up with at least three things that you're grateful for in your life. They can be big or small. You can change them every day; in fact, I encourage you to always be looking for something different to be grateful for. Ultimately, listen to your heart, and whatever comes out cannot be wrong. Do your best to say it like you mean it even if you're not feeling it. As they say, "Fake it till you make it." Think of emotion as the fuel behind your words, propelling you closer to the things you desire with greater speed. You will make it if you keep this up, that's for sure.

When I started my journey, I found this part to be very easy, which is one of the reasons I put it first. That, and all of the other truths and principles work better if you're in state of gratitude. In fact, if you are truly in a state of gratitude, you really can't mess up any of this. No matter how fat, tired, or lazy I may have felt on a given day, I always thought it easy to look into the mirror and say, "Today and every day I am open to receive all of the abundance and beautiful gifts the universe has for me." I would then stumble into the shower and name five or ten things I was grateful for. Some days all I could come up with was the same five things: my kids, my wife, my family, my house, and my vehicle, but as I started implementing this practice every day, I realized two things. One, those five things meant the world to me. Two, there were many, many more things to be grateful for. The more I did this, the more I became aware of things to be grateful for, and the more good things and people flowed into my life.

This is like the phenomenon of what happens when you buy a new car. All of the sudden, everyone seems to be driving the same car, same color even. No, everyone didn't rush out and buy the same car as you, you are just more aware, which is the topic of the next chapter—and awareness of gratitude is a beautiful thing because it just keeps getting better and better.

You will find your gratitude list growing and growing as you stretch out and work this fabulous muscle.

And so it is.

*"Three things cannot be long hidden: the sun,
the moon, and the truth."* —Buddha

• • • • • •

AWARENESS

Simple Truth 2
It is far easier to change that
which we are aware of.

AWARENESS IS THE next step forward into the light. It starts with a pure and real honesty with one's self. It is only through awareness that we can start identifying the things in our lives that are not working the way we desire them to be.

As we discussed earlier, it's the power of our thoughts that enables us to manifest the things and situations in our lives. So how do you have the right thoughts? It starts with your communication. How you communicate a thought is sometimes even more important than the thought itself because you are now potentially influencing one or more people outside of your mind. If you are in a position of authority or leadership or just around people who value your opinion, you could be negatively affecting the way other people look at things and therefore think, so I would encourage you to act with great care with your words and think before you speak.

Of course, communication with the outside world is just the tip of the iceberg. It's just the part of our communication that we allow ourselves to expose to the outside world. As the saying goes, talk is cheap (but still powerful). Where the real story lies is in the way we communicate with ourselves. It is our inner dialogue, or our self-talk, that's the most important thing to be aware of, as all of our thoughts and words will be a result of that.

At some point in your journey, and not necessarily in the very beginning when you may be weaker, you will have to create a sense of possibility in your mind. An inner expectation that the things you desire to appear in your life not only can but will appear. As we start choosing the right and empowering words, this expectation will naturally get stronger and we will eventually get to that incredible place called *knowing*. The kind of knowing where something doesn't need to be proved to you any further. You just know it is going to happen. It's through this knowing that intention takes over and you do whatever it takes to get the job done.

Take your job, for example. When you go to work, do you expect to make it to Friday (most weeks anyway) even if you are having a less than perfect Monday? Unless you want to end up on the wrong side of that unemployment ratio we were talking about, of course, you expect to make it to Friday. In fact, you probably expect to make it at least to that second Friday when you get your check, right? It's what you expect even though you have no idea what's going to happen between now and then. You will push through whatever gets in your way and do whatever it takes. It's what you expect, and it's what you get.

That part is straightforward. Now, where the possibility comes in is when you realize you can expect to have a great

Monday and manifest *that* into reality. This all comes down to the way you communicate with yourself. On the way to work, are you thinking about the difficult person you're going to have to deal with again? Or are you thinking that this is going to be an incredible week, and focusing in on all of the wonderful experiences you intend to have and all of the great things you intend to get done? You see, we tend to expect to have a certain experience in life and *then* bring it into creation. We will look for supporting evidence all around us to bring this expected experience into reality. We are all like trial lawyers when it comes to this skill. We can convince ourselves, and many around us, of anything by extracting just the data around us that fits our expectations, or our "argument." Again, you will use this very nimble skill to your advantage very soon. It is through a mindful auditing of your thoughts that you can start to create a shift in your expectations and therefore your experiences.

Another helpful hint is to be aware of your emotions. It has been said that we have over sixty thousand thoughts per day. That's a pretty large task to be aware of each and every one, much less to be able to audit them all. No, you will certainly miss some, and most of them are unimportant anyway; however, another helpful approach is to monitor your emotions as they come to you. If you are in a state of joy, it is highly likely that you are communicating very well with yourself, and probably others, too. If you're feeling bad or depressed, that is probably a time to be looking at the thoughts you're having and how you can shift them.

Also, be aware of the people you are around. Most people tend to be of the same spirit and attitude most of the time (i.e., we tend to have the same 60,000 thoughts every day). If you find yourself constantly around people who are this way all the time, it's normal for your thoughts to align with theirs, even if only temporarily. I've found that the majority of my feelings or emotions have much to do with who I'm near and the conversations we have. The more positive, uplifting, and encouraging people I can surround myself with, the less I have to be concerned with having the right thoughts in any given moment.

I do realize that you can't get all the negative people out of your life. They are all part of the perfect balance in our world. It's only through the contrast of the undesired that we truly are able to appreciate the desired. Appreciate the negative people for that. Wish them well, silently if need be, and change the subject or move along. I also know that you may not always be able to get away from some of these people, and that's OK, too. Just be aware and extra careful to not participate in their game. You'll find that they will usually go away if they don't find you a willing participant.

If you take this into the realm of eating, an awareness of our habits will serve to change your actions. When I started my journey, one of the first things I had to do was to consciously become aware of the pace at which I was eating. I needed to slow down. Well before I ever needed to focus on what I was eating, I needed to focus on *how* I was eating. I shoveled down my food, many times getting through two or more plates before anyone else had finished their first. It was no wonder I was twice the size. So the first thing I did was retrain myself on how to eat. I started watching others eat and tried to keep pace with some of the slower eaters at the table. I mindfully chewed my food. I tasted each bite. I started to notice the colors and the smells. I put my fork down between bites, chewed completely, and swallowed before putting the next bite in my mouth. I know it may sound silly, but I started to take notice of the conversations going on at the table and realized there was no need to be in such a rush. It was just one of the many techniques my body utilized to stay at that massive weight I had so successfully achieved. I was relearning to eat, just like a person in physical rehabilitation may have to learn to walk again. Step by step I got there, but not without some falling down.

Some of these habits may sound all too familiar, but there is good news. Practice a little mindfulness and you can turn all of that around—and enjoy your meal a lot more, as well. This concept, although completely necessary, was foreign to me. It felt like signing my name with my left hand. But, like any skill, it grew with time. That's not to say that sometimes I don't find myself eating too fast even to this day; it's just that my level of awareness is extremely heightened now and I can see it more clearly. As a result I can alter my behavior much sooner. This would never happen if it hadn't been brought to my attention in the first place.

A Foundation of Trust

I found it imperative to my healing to have an awareness of what I was eating. It is far too easy to let the foods we snack on all day long or the quantities we eat get out of control. So, when I started, I wrote down every last morsel I ate in a food log. Talk about awareness. That was when I could start to see the mass of food and drink coming in. It's so easy for overweight people to simply blame their weight on their slow metabolism or bad genetics until we start paying careful attention to our eating habits.

I found this technique a heck of a lot easier than following some ridiculous diet plan that had me eating rice cakes and grapefruit. I didn't tell myself that I had to stop eating anything, just that I had to be honest with myself and write it down. Just the act of writing it down greatly altered my food intake as well as what I was eating—and yes, to this day, every day, I write down everything I eat. Will I keep this up for the rest of my life? I don't know what the rest of my life is going to look like, and I am open to whatever great things the universe has in store for me. But if it helps me to stay at a health and fitness level that makes me feel good, then I am willing, absolutely. Just as I am willing to let my accountant keep track of my finances and taxes, I will keep track of my food intake. I view it as taking personal responsibility. Remember, I'm not telling you to do anything. I'm telling you what worked for me. It's nothing more than practiced mindfulness. Later I will explain in greater detail how I wrote it down.

You'd be amazed at what you're really eating. You have to be willing to be honest with yourself here and write down everything, even what you drink. It is my belief that if you do nothing else but write down what you eat, just the elevated awareness will move you significantly in the direction of your desired weight over an extended period of time.

If you're like me, you've probably made all kinds of promises to yourself in the past and broken them. You may not take yourself seriously anymore, and certainly you don't trust yourself if you've been in and out of this pattern repeatedly. If you can't trust someone, you will have a hard time accepting them unconditionally and ultimately loving them. Make no mistake about it, underline it, mark it in bold, write this down and carry it in your pocket so that you don't forget:

This entire transformational journey is about learning to love yourself again, perhaps for the first time in a very long time, and it needs to be built on a foundation of trust.

By being honest with yourself on a daily basis and consistently writing down what you eat, you start to rebuild that foundation, and it becomes impossible to blame your perceived lack of self-control around food on anyone or anything else. This is because at no point is anyone restricting you in any way. Nobody is taking anything from you, including whatever you're eating. The only thing you have to do to start building this trust is to simply write down what you eat. However bad you may think that list looks, write it down. Just the simple act of consistently writing down what you eat will start to alter your habits enough that you will start moving your weight in the right direction without consciously changing anything else, including what you're eating. Now, that shows you how powerful a factor awareness can be in your life.

This is the kind of "easy" I was talking about when I started down this road. This was a very achievable and attainable goal for me, and one that I built off of and grew from. This was the first step in learning to trust myself again. Even more importantly, it was the first step in learning to love myself, perhaps for the first time that I could remember.

Weigh and Keep Going

Another habit I had to become aware of was where, when, and how I was using food. I would eat in the car, at my desk, on the couch, standing up in the kitchen, while making dinner, while cleaning up dishes, basically anywhere and everywhere. I had to take note and be aware of these habits, and then keep my eating limited to a designated eating area. Like the dinner table. Again, this, in my mind, was easy. I wasn't telling myself I couldn't eat this or that, just that I had to slow down, write it down, and sit down. I could do that. Now I was really starting to get some traction and my successes were building on top of each other—and I still hadn't resorted to rice cakes and grapefruit (I do like grapefruit).

This brought me to another awareness that it was time to face: my actual weight. I supposed that if I was going to get to a normal weight, it would, at some point, be helpful to know where I started from. So I weighed. This hurt. I didn't think the number was going to be as high as it was. I wondered how high it had ever gotten. I wrote it down, wiped the tears away, and kept going.

I said it would be easy, not always pleasant. So weigh, and then get off the scale and don't worry; we'll get you to a place where you like the number you see, but more importantly to where you like what you see in the mirror and how you feel, which is the only measure that really matters in my mind. It's just going to take a little time and a little patience. It's difficult to get where we're going when we don't know where we currently are. Besides, trust me, you'll want to know what that number is later. You will be very proud of yourself, and others will want to know how much weight you have released. This will be a source of great inspiration for many people.

A word on weighing yourself: as you may have gathered by now, I did not go on a crash diet, and though weight did fall off rather quickly for me, faster than I thought it would, at times it did not. Some weeks it went up. Some weeks it went up quite a bit. It was not uncommon for my weight to go five to seven pounds in either direction on any given day. Your weight will fluctuate, and it can mess with your mind. You may even gain some weight from time to time. That's OK. On your journey of a thousand miles, you may trip, stumble, might even stub a toe or two if you're not wearing shoes. It's normal. Keep going, and for the love of God, don't weigh yourself every day! Weigh once a week, maximum. Pick the same day and the same time. Stick to the morning, if you can, before eating. Try to keep salt intake down the day before. I like weighing on Monday morning because it helps me to be extra mindful over the weekends, when I am prone to overeating. I know I will have to look at that number on Monday, and I want to see a lower number. Just take care not to put too much energy into that number. Any number of things can happen to push it around from day to day, and it doesn't necessarily equate to fat loss or gain. Your water levels constantly fluctuate, and so will your weight. That's normal. You should be more concerned with the bigger trends of where that number is going, month to month rather than week to week. OK, enough about that dirty scale. Put it back in the cabinet under your toilet bowl cleaner. Don't worry; you'll get to be good friends with Mr. Scaley, eventually.

Peace and Satisfaction

Another area to be aware of is the reasons why you eat. I know what you may be thinking: "I eat because I'm hungry...and I get *really* hungry." But I'd ask you to examine the circumstances surrounding the times you eat or maybe overeat. Are you feeling stress when this occurs? Depression? Anger? Or something along these lines? If so, eating is certainly not the answer long term. One simple little tool I used was a quick meditation when I found myself emotionally eating.

I would close my eyes and focus on my breath. I would take a deep breath in and walk away from the food for just a minute. Many times this is all it takes to just slow you down before you're elbow deep in a family size bag of Doritos (like you were planning on sharing those with your family), wiping the orange stained cheetle off your fingertips and onto your jeans while chasing it down with a cold Coke as you collapse on the couch and your eyes roll back in your head. Sometimes just taking some breaths and walking away for a minute will be enough to stop that chain of events—a chain that will no doubt leave you feeling just as empty as when you started, only more depressed or angry because you let yourself down again. Interestingly enough, those simple carbohydrates and sugars only make you hungrier than when you started.

I always felt like I was trying to fill myself up, no matter what or when I was eating. It was usually not just hunger I was trying to satisfy. There was definitely an emptiness I was trying to fill. I was eating more for a feeling than for just the need of some sustenance. It was this awareness, just my acknowledgement of it, that ultimately led to the healing that needed to take place. That will all come in time, and later I'll go over some different things that can help you cope and move through feelings like this without suppressing or ignoring them.

*"Only in quiet waters do things mirror themselves undistorted.
Only in a quiet mind is adequate perception of the world."*
—*Hans Margolius*

Meditation is a great way to calm your mind and help you be more aware. It is the easiest way I've found to clear the window to your soul, to communicate with your heart. It's one of the most powerful techniques to help bring about inner peace, and I know that for myself, at least, inner peace was missing. I was trying to self-medicate with food when all I really wanted was peace and satisfaction. I started to take five minutes per day in a quiet place just to try to still my mind and quiet myself. To have spent a little more time on this would have probably served me even better, but I had made a deal with myself that this was going to be easy and I figured at the time, "Who has time for thirty minutes of meditation?" Not to mention it can be difficult to quiet your mind for that long if you're not used to it. So, I did five minutes. Even two minutes will work if that's all you can manage. The important thing is to take time daily and add this to your routine. The results will be far reaching and the effort involved is minimal.

The Resistance Factor

When you start telling people what, how much, and when they must eat, as soon as their bodies don't agree with that schedule or plan, there is immediate resistance, and an instantaneous breakdown of the system ensues. This is a most important concept to be aware of. Resistance is always met with resistance. When I supplied no resistance, I moved forward quickly with nothing to slow me down. I then started to create a resistance-free plan for myself to follow, piece by piece. Your body, your ego, your mind—none of them want to be told what to do. The moment your ego and your body get on the same team, your timid and perhaps weak intent will eventually be steamrolled…every time. Don't set up a game you're likely to lose. This is why 95 percent of diets fail. Even when they succeed, five percent of the time, it's usually because the dieter eventually gets this concept and stops viewing the routine as a challenge and instead actually starts to enjoy the process. After all, this is why we're here: to enjoy the process of life, not agonize over it.

This resistance factor holds true in any area of your life. The moment you start pushing for or against anything else, you will always be met with an equal or greater amount of resistance. This is another reason why I don't use the term "weight loss" or call it a "battle" or a "fight" because this is simply mentally preparing for a resistance. That's what you get when you engage in a fight. Instead, I choose to be more like water and flow around the problems I encounter.

The entire act of releasing, be it weight, fear, problems, anything you don't want in your life experience, is all about removing resistance. You will find that, without the resistance, everything comes to you quickly and effortlessly. You will soon find that it is none other than yourself who applies the resistance through your thoughts and reactions to things happening around you. This leads to fear. Fear can be released just like any other emotion. Acknowledge your fears, challenges, and difficult situations, and then act as if you were watching them from outside yourself. Just watch yourself flow right around them.

Remember you can always meditate anytime you like, even for a moment or two to reconnect with your wiser, stronger inner self and to bring about the inner peace required to make it through any situation. I recommend an excellent book by Dr. Wayne Dyer, *Getting in the Gap*, to learn more about this subject, which will spill over into and benefit every aspect of your life. The more connected you can get with your inner self, the happier you have to be because happiness and healthiness is your true nature and all your inner self knows.

So you've learned to be consciously aware of your communication, especially with yourself, and to be aware of your activity levels and eating habits. You will have made great progress by this time, and it will all have been done easily. Your progress may or may not be showing up on the scale by this point, but it makes no difference. You are starting to heal from the inside out and it may take some a little longer to see the changes on the outside. It really depends on how well you flow with these ideas and how little resistance you offer to the process. It all can be done effortlessly if you allow it to be. Just remember, if anything along your path feels difficult, like you're fighting an uphill battle, trying too hard, or gripping too tight, rethink the words you're using. Remember to breathe. Let the tension flow out of your body and start again. If you're hungry, eat. If you're tired, rest. As you improve and find your choices naturally changing, you will realize that life does not need to be a struggle and that many people don't have to struggle to keep their weight normal. Neither do you.

In the past, I hadn't realized all the things I was doing that weren't in alignment with my intentions. Some of them were small and perhaps seemingly insignificant, but the cumulative effect was very significant.

> *"It is the little things that count and many little things make a big thing." —Raymond Hollowell*

I developed a couple of great skills in awareness that I'll share with you right now. I didn't start using these immediately, only because I wasn't aware of the bad habits I was practicing or that there were simple alternatives. In hindsight, I would recommend you implement some of these things right away because they are easy and will help you with mindfulness and hunger control.

1. Eat on smaller plates. This is an easy one. I'm not suggesting it's a silver bullet, but it is easy and will help some of the time. The result? Even if you do eat two plates of food, there was obviously less on each plate, so you've cut down your caloric intake without any effort. I even started using teaspoons and salad forks to minimize my bite sizes. Every little bit counts.

2. Leave the serving dish in the kitchen. Put the food on your plate and bring the plate to the dinner table. You are far more likely to eat less this way. There's a great book by Brian Wansink called *Mindless Eating* that speaks in depth about many great tips like this. I do suggest, however, you keep the vegetables, salad, or fruit on the table as well as a pitcher of water. These things you will want to increase your consumption of, so keep them close by.

3. Drink a glass of water ten minutes before your meal. Think of this as a speed bump to slow you down and ensure you're not mistaking thirst for hunger. You can also try a small handful of nuts or seeds. I suggest natural unsalted pumpkin seeds. The fat in the seeds will help get that message to your brain that some good quality nutrients are coming and to go ahead and shut down hunger signals. You would be amazed at how well this works. Just don't eat too many of these nuts or seeds, as they are high in calories. Be sure to always measure out a food like this so that you can be aware of how much you've taken in. Remember, these nuts are not intended to fill you up, just slow you down a little bit so that you aren't ravenous when you finally sit down to eat that delicious meal.

4. Always be aware of how much a serving size is and how much you are getting ready to consume. Even if you are going to eat multiple servings, you owe it to yourself to know just how many servings and calories you're consuming. If you want three servings of cereal, so be it. But don't try to fool yourself into thinking that one heaping, oversized bowl was just a serving. Remember self-honesty and personal responsibility. It only takes a moment to figure out what eight ounces or two tablespoons or half a cup looks and feels like. You won't have to measure out these things all the time, just a couple of times until you get the feel of it. There are resources for looking up serving sizes and nutritional information that you can find at www.SixSimpleTruths.com under Resources.

5. Always portion out your food. Never eat out of the bigger package. This is called acting with intention. If you intend to eat something, then intend how much you want to eat, put that much in a bowl, cup, or bag, and put the rest back. All too often we sit mindlessly elbow deep in a bag of something, and before we know it, we've eaten even more than we cared to eat. Pay attention and scoop out how much you want, no matter what it is you're eating.

6. Eat only in designated eating areas. This means not on the couch, in the car, at your desk, or during work. This is all part of mindful eating—and slowing down. Pay attention to your food. When you sit down in an intended place to eat, you've set the tone and expressed your intention. You've sent the message to the universe that says, "OK, I'm ready to eat and I'm going to be respectful of the food that is before me," as opposed to shoveling the food down while zoned out watching TV.

7. Eat your veggies first and have them cover about half your plate. The other half should be composed of half protein and half carbohydrate. Though vegetables may seem odd, if you eat them first by the time you get to the main course, you'll be half full and the smaller portion will satisfy you just fine.

8. One great mindful tip is to breathe. That's right, breathe. This one is *big*. When you feel overwhelming hunger or the urge to eat, stop and take a break. Close your eyes and take a deep breath then slowly release it. Slowly open your eyes back up, and you will have a fresh, new look at the world. The oxygen will get to your brain, but most importantly, it will center you and bring you into the present moment. Notice the feelings you are having and where they're coming from. Be aware of the emotional eating habits and feelings, and breathe them right out of your body. Breathe out the stress and the tension. You can combine breathing and meditation with a simple yellow green meditation. It only takes a minute but you can do it for as long as you like. Close your eyes and uncross your legs, hands, and arms. Get quiet and take a couple of deep breaths. Take a full breath in and visualize yourself breathing in the color green, a calm, relaxing green like that of the trees or grass from the earth. Picture green filling up your lungs and then being sent all through your body to every cell, bringing a calm energy to every cell. When you breathe out, visualize yourself breathing out the color yellow, a high-energy color, and let any stress or negative feelings out of your body along with the color yellow. Overeating **will be the last thing on your mind.**

9. Put tempting food away. There is great wisdom in the words "out of sight, out of mind." This was another great tip I picked up from *Mindless Eating.* The idea is, according to Brian Wansink, that you make roughly two hundred food decisions every day. Every time you see a candy dish, every time you open the refrigerator, every time you see a box of cookies, you either partake or you don't. You either decide to eat or not, or decide to purchase food or not. All day long you are making decisions that will affect what food comes into not only your house or car, but more importantly, into your body. The good news is that you succeed in making the right decision much of the time, probably more often than not. The bad news is, regardless of how often you make the right decision, it only takes a couple of bad decisions to keep you where you are or even push you farther away. So what do you do, stop making food decisions? Of course not. You have to. Your survival depends on it. But what if you were to cut your food decisions from two hundred down to only seventy-five or one hundred? What would happen then? You would automatically eliminate half of your mistakes. How do you do it? Simple: put the box of cookies out of sight. You will inevitably pass that bag of cookies ten or twenty times as you walk by the kitchen. That's ten or twenty decisions. When you put the bag in the cabinet, that's only one decision. Get it? You can apply this to candy dishes, food on the table, you name it. Now, to stay focused on what you do want, put fresh fruit and bottled water everywhere around you, and you will start seeing many more good food decisions come your way. What we see, we think about. What we think about, we bring about. What are you seeing?

"Change the way you look at things and the things
you look at will change" —Wayne Dyer

You have a good solid foundation to start off with. There is farther to go, but it becomes far more rewarding from this point. You have opened yourself up to receive, and now you are slowly, always smoothly, starting to become aware of the patterns that have created the reality you wish to change. Now we'll move into the underlying emotions and fears and learn to loosen our grip and let go.

"Your nature is truth, and when you oppose it, you don't feel like yourself. Stress never feels as natural as peace does." — Byron Katie

• • • • • •

RELEASE

Simple Truth 3
To be satisfied, one need only release
what is not in one's true nature.

TO RELEASE IS the most natural thing in the world. We're all
born with the ability to let go. Releasing is what this book is all
about. It empowers us to be able to completely relinquish that
which does not move us closer to our desires.

Notice I said *relinquish*, not *suppress*. Suppression is what
so many of us have done for so many years. We've suppressed
emotions and feelings from the time we were little, from the
moment someone told us to stop crying or not to yell. We've
been mastering the craft ever since then and have seldom
looked back. Most of us have a lifetime of suppression under
our belts—but no need to worry. It can all be let go in a moment once we've become aware and allowed it to go.

When something is truly released, it is unconditionally let
go of. That means it never has to come back if you've fully let
it happen. Many times in my journey I thought I had fully
released something only to find the same problem resurfacing

at a later date. I would think all was lost and that somehow I must have messed this up.

You will not mess this up. This is a process that will be different for everyone. No two people are the same, and I've found there are as many different ways to release weight as there are people who would like to release weight. You may find that you have to keep coming back to certain issues and digging a bit deeper. Many people refer to it as peeling back different layers, like an onion. You need not be discouraged to have a fear or a dysfunctional habit return to your life after you thought you had released it. Just realize that you're working through a process, and so there may be a little more work to do in your process.

This was very evident for me when I came close to my ideal weight. I somehow would keep finding small things resurfacing and holding me back. What I discovered was that I was attracting these things into my life. It was all me—I was not allowing the final pounds to release. I had to get very quiet and really listen to my inner wisdom get this point. I had a deeper level of release to hit, another layer of the onion to peel away. Once I did, I found that the remaining pounds once again started to drop off.

Let me emphasize that it did not come from working harder or fighting myself. I had the mindset that I was going to have to really bust it to get the last fifteen pounds off, that I would have to work out extra long and extra hard and limit what I was eating, all in an effort to get quicker results. It just didn't work that way. It never works that way. I was resorting to my old ways of trying to "lose" weight.

The good news is this: release is actually much easier than that. Here I was banging my head against the wall trying so hard to complete my transformation, when the answer was not "more and harder" but "less and easier." The best way I can describe it was that I just finally loosened my grip and let it go.

Many of us hold on to our fat as a barrier, as a protective shield against all that may threaten us. And though I had released so much of it, my body, or my mind, was resistant to letting the last little bit go because it was all I had left of my old defense mechanism. But I no longer needed to defend myself because there was no longer a fight. All I had were old and unproductive habits left to be let go of. I had not found anyone to guide me through this process at the time, even though the help was there, but you have the benefit of my experience. It is my intention that you find hope in these pages that helps you to let go. You have everything you need to do it. You just need to get quiet and listen.

Release is found through tranquility and serenity. It can found through quieting your mind and meditating. Before you get into one of the very simple processes of release, it would serve you well to first identify, or become aware of, the areas in your life that need releasing. They tend to be common among many of us, especially those of us who share the common bond of having been overweight.

We've talked about becoming aware of negative self-talk. Well, one of the things that's bred from negative self-talk is our own limiting beliefs. This is the self-doubt we impose on ourselves that stops us from reaching our full potential, which is limitless. Our ego is hard at work to keep us safe by stopping us from taking too many risks or from putting ourselves out there, which is, of course, the only way we can grow and advance from where we currently are. Our ego builds a hard shell around us, and when it sees us start to wander or stretch outside our comfort zone, it jumps in and says, "You can't do that" or "You might get hurt" or "No one else in your family has done that." It will make up any excuse it thinks you may buy to get you to stop this new and presumably risky behavior and to get you back into your comfort zone, where it feels you belong and where it feels safe and comfy. Get it?

Your ego can get loud and boisterous. It can get intimidating and convincing. It can badger and scare you right out of your pants if you let it. But take heed: this dog has no teeth and it's tethered with a thick chain to a steel pole in your mind. Eventually, we're going to cut him loose and just let him run off and out of your life, but for now, just know that it's all bark and no bite...really. Nothing is awful is going to happen to you as a result of following anything I'm suggesting here. You may get a little bumped and scraped from taking risks you wouldn't have otherwise taken, but it's nothing that isn't well worth it.

Whenever I'm feeling fear or anxiety over taking a new risk, I keep in mind that nothing can be more painful than where I started from, and that was where my ego had taken me. That was where my ego was trying to keep me. But I wasn't safe. I was dying a slow and miserable death. The interesting thing about fear is that most of the time, there's really nothing to be afraid of at all. Like Hale Dwoskin, of the legendary Sedona Method (which we'll discuss), says, most of the things that we're afraid of have the consistency of a soap bubble. They look real and they look like they take up space and have substance, but if you'll only delve right into the middle of them they simply pop and disappear. Oh yes, your ego is a wonderful bubble machine, but just remember, they're only bubbles. My little children love to play with bubbles. So far, they haven't gotten hurt from them.

RELEASE

· · · · · ·

So this is what we're going to do; we're going to dive right into the center. And once you've become aware how easy it can be to release, you'll find that the resistance you've been creating in the past will simply disappear, just like the popped bubble. It is in this release and this disappearing of resistance that you will reach the feeling that eludes so many when it comes to weight release. Oh yes…the ultra light and free feeling of the coveted "effortless ease."

This is the part people want to understand most when I tell them that my weight release came about with effortless ease. Many respond in disbelief: "Surely, you must have worked very, very hard at it. Weight loss doesn't just come about that easily." Yes, they are correct in saying that. Weight "loss" does not come about that easy, usually. Weight release, well, that's a different story. You've seen what I've done so far. Did any of it seem hard to you? No. That's because it wasn't. It was all done with effortless ease…the proverbial Garden of Eden that most think does not even exist. Let me be perfectly clear. That is one of the first thoughts you will have to release and replace with a better statement of trust. You can release your excess weight with effortless ease (and have fun doing it). I am here to tell you with 100 percent certainty that fat release with this kind of effortless ease *does* exist, and it's easier than you may think. We all need to be careful to not have such rigid thinking. After all, we once thought the earth was flat and the sun moved around the earth.

"Minds are like parachutes. They only function when open."—
Tommy Dewar, Scottish whiskey distiller

Telling Your Story

Let's first look at your story. This is a most powerful concept to get because we define who we are when we retell our story. We all have one, don't we? No? Let me ask you a question then, and I want you to think very carefully about your answers. Why are you overweight? I mean, aside from the fact that you may (or may not) eat too many calories for the amount of energy you put out. Why? What caused this? You don't have to stop there: why don't you have the money you'd like or the job you really want or the people in your life you may want to have there or perhaps live where you'd prefer or whatever it is in your life that is not in perfect alignment with your true heart's desires? Why? Why is it that way? You tell bits and pieces of your story every day, and you are a master at getting the details right on this story. You embellish it and refine it with perfect clarity and vision. You make up reasons (or excuses) to fill in any blanks that could possibly show up. Yes, this story is complete and full and will explain any of the details of your life that anyone wants to know. You could, and many do—I did—write a book about your story. Nobody could tell it as well as you.

Of course, you probably have some successes, too, right? I mean, most of us have some good things that even we can admit to. These things become part of your story, too, to balance it out and give it validity. I mean, this story is nothing if not real, the God's honest truth. The way you tell it, you could sell it to a Hollywood producer (some people actually have).

What I came to realize is that when the good things that I thought balanced out the deficiencies were pulled away, I became very insecure and realized that my identity was just that, an identity. It wasn't me any more than my driver's license was me. It was just an identity, a representation from a certain point of observation. I was giving far too much weight to a story that didn't hold water. Talk is cheap, but powerful.

So, what is your story? Abused? Neglected? Bullied? Pushed around? Oppressed? Depressed? Suppressed? Not given all the opportunities you would have liked? Not treated well? Grew up in the wrong part of town or perhaps the right part of town with the wrong people? Had parents that messed you up? (You're not alone in feeling that way.) You know your story well. There are more stories than there are people, and they're all true, right?

Wrong. It's just a story. The author in this case is again your ego, mostly, trying to protect you from anything and everything that it thinks can or will go wrong. If you aren't satisfied with where your story has led you, I would encourage you to take that story and rewrite it. When it came to my health, and other areas of my life, my story was just not working for me anymore. It hadn't kept me safe. It was killing me. I scrapped it. Of course, I didn't scrap all of the people or events, just the way I perceived them. I rewrote it, word by word, piece by piece.

Next time you find yourself retelling the old story, instead become aware and make a conscious effort to stop and correct yourself. Use words that are more empowering. This story is the first thing you need to release because within it is the basis for everything that holds you back from living the life you desire. Within it also lie the keys to open any door you desire.

You have the good in your life because you attracted it to you. You'll remember the first step was to identify the good in your life and be grateful for it. Focus on this good, hold it firm, and everything else in this story, release. If you do nothing but detach yourself from this story, your life will improve immediately. All of your negative self-communications are the limiting factors in your story. Just let them go.

Emotions we hold tight to can also be released. In all truthfulness, anything can be released. I'm going to hit the most significant topics that came up in my release work, but do realize that it may be something completely different for you. This, too, can just as easily be released.

When we experience emotions like anger or sadness, we do two things. First, we provide emotional fuel to a negative feeling. This is a very effective way of quickly attracting more of the undesired thing, for what works for good feelings works just as well for bad. Unfortunately, we sometimes tend to get more passionate about the negative than the positive. This is something to be aware of. When is the last time you heard someone screaming at the top of their lungs about how happy they were?

The second thing we do is say things like, "I'm angry" or "I'm sad." We've discussed the harm in this negative self-communication, but what I haven't mentioned is how literal your mind and the universal mind will take your words. *You* are not anger. You may be feeling that way at the moment, but *you* are not the emotion. *You* are not sadness, itself. Again, you may feel that way, but it is not you and you are not it. In fifteen minutes you'll probably be feeling a different emotion.

We are not our emotions. However, we tell ourselves all day long that we are, and that's how the universe hears us communicate. That's also how we hear ourselves communicate, and we will attract more of that right to our experience.

RELEASE

● ● ● ● ● ●

"You are not your...khakis." — *Tyler Durden*

The fact is, you are not your emotions. You are not your things. You are not your relationships. You are not your situations. You are a perfect creation. You are a beautiful manifestation of the universal mind. You came here with beautiful and unique talents and gifts built right into you. *That* is what you are. You came about by no accident and you are definitely *not* anger. But when you constantly reinforce this negative concept over and over and over again, it eventually becomes part of your story and you buy it yourself. Then you turn around and sell it to others...to anyone who will listen. If they don't buy it, you say there's something wrong with them and, like a diligent salesperson, move on to the next sale with the mantra, *"No means next."* Everyone else has their stories, too. This makes your story that much more believable. So again, be mindful of your emotions and to not associate them with who you are. If you find that you are, simply release that thought and remember that you may have a story, but you are not your story.

People, too, can be a large part of how we get shaped and molded, even as adults. And though nobody can do your thinking for you, and therefore attract anything for you, they can certainly influence your thoughts. You can, however, attract people, and with those people come the things that they attract. An example of this would be going out for a couple of drinks with a friend. They have a little too much to drink, drive, and get in an accident, and you get physically harmed. How did you attract that? You attracted the person who attracted the event. I'll also remind you that, in this scenario, you were participating in the event that led up to the accident, as well. Bam! Attracted.

Here's the good news: people and their negative beliefs can all be released as well. That's right. You don't have to purchase their story or, even worse, weave it into yours. It's just not necessary. The people who are not contributing toward your perfect health, emotional or physical, will become evident as you progress along your path. Those folks will either need to grow and change and support the new, healthy you, or you will need to be able to flow around their energy somehow, sometimes by removing yourself from their presence, if only temporarily.

Just remember, everyone in your life has played some role. Many have supported you. Some have contributed to your lack of progress with their thoughts and energy. Most have just kind of hung out at about the same place you were at, while some were there all along trying to uplift you. You know the difference, and you know who is who. One of the most exciting parts of this journey will be in the helping of others to get to better places in their lives, as well. For now, just realize that you can release other people's thoughts for you.

The Healing Power of Forgiveness

When it comes to other people, living or dead, near or far away, there is a topic I must bring up or I'd be remiss. I'm talking about the healing power of forgiveness. Let's face it, we were shaped and influenced and molded, especially as children, by the people around us, and sometimes we wish that they had made some different choices. Forgiveness is a crucial element in being able to truly release and move forward in many cases.

What so many of us do when we've been the victim of some type of wrongdoing, be it intentional or not, is to avoid thinking about what went wrong or our need to address it. We say things like, "What's done is done" or "I can't go back and change it" or "That was water under the bridge, so what good does it do to dwell on it?" Well, perhaps all of that is true, but in one form or another it is highly probable that we're actually suppressing our real emotions. This is very often mistaken for releasing. But we're still angry or depressed or upset.

Whatever you've been through, realize that other people have experienced something similar. Also, take strength in the knowledge that someone else has not only struggled with the same things but risen above them to lead a happy and healthy life. You can, too. When it comes to the wrongs you've been dealt, usually one of the deeper levels of growth comes in the form of forgiveness. It is through forgiveness that you can allow yourself to move on. Understand that people are usually doing the best they can with the limited knowledge they have and the influencing factors in their life.

Forgiveness does not mean justifying or condoning the act of oppression, aggression, or whatever it was. Let me be perfectly clear: you should in no way be willing to let the unacceptable behavior continue. But it is only through forgiveness that you can truly start to heal from the inside out. Don't worry if this one doesn't come to you right away, like many of the other things you are learning will. Just be aware that for you to truly release some of the things in your life that pertain to other people, at some point you'll have to forgive. There is incredible freedom in the process, and you will immediately begin to feel lighter in every way imaginable. Some of our anger and disappointment is buried so deep that it manifests in ways we may not recognize. Shame and guilt and other low-level energies often create a lack of self-love that will allow you to create a body that is void of the health you deserve. Sometimes all you need to do is forgive, and things can start to correct themselves and heal immediately. Again, this isn't something have you have to struggle with, just to be aware of. When you are ready, you will know what to do. This, too, can come to you with effortless ease as you move from gratitude to awareness to release.

I believe it is also important to point out that the type of forgiveness I speak of is much more beneficial for the one doing the forgiving. You are doing this for you, not for them. Forgiveness is a very deep and meaningful type of release because many times it allows that person or event out of your mind and out of your heart. This is not to be taken lightly or glanced over. You may do well to meditate over it. The answers all lie within your heart if you can get quiet and listen. This is all part of trusting your heart.

The simplest form of release has been taught and practiced by a gentleman by the name of Hale Dwoskin of the Sedona Method. I will briefly explain one of the processes but would strongly encourage you to visit his Web site, read his book, and dive deeper into his work to get a better understanding of how to fully utilize this method. It is so incredibly simple that it can be deceiving. Like I told you in the beginning, the truth is simple. That simplicity is probably the single biggest block to truly getting any of the ideas and concepts herein. We tend to make things difficult or complicated. That would much more easily and painlessly explain why this peace has eluded us for so long and caused us so much trouble. So here we go.

> *"The truth is simple. If it were complicated, everyone would understand it."* — *Walt Whitman*

RELEASE

· · · · · ·

First, start by grabbing a small object nearby. Right now, pick up something like a pen or pencil, hold it in your hand, and grip it tightly. Don't let go until I ask you to. Also, don't think about gripping the pen. This pen is representing the things in your life that are not working for you, not allowing you to be as healthy or happy as you deserve to be. You may have been holding these things for years and years. What happens after a while is that you start to feel like this thing is a part of you. It feels like you and it are one, even though, logically, you know this not to be the case. You are holding this pen, but you are not this pen. Again, remember, your subconscious mind is not concerned with the difference between what is real and what is only perceived. This is the reason you can salivate while only *thinking* of biting into a tart, juicy lemon. It's the reason you can cry or laugh while watching a movie. Your subconscious mind can't distinguish between a feeling and a reality, which we will address later and use to our advantage. For now, just know that your mind will hold tight to things and assimilate them as though they are a part of you. Now, hold your arm out straight, palm down with pen gripped just as tightly. Hand cramped yet? Now, open your hand and let the object fall to the ground. Emotional release is just that simple.

Think of a situation or feeling that you have that brings you pain or discomfort. Please, go slowly here. Hold that image clear in your mind just like you held that pen. Now, as best you can, just allow the associated feelings to be present. It's OK to feel that way. Just for a moment, have no desire to change them. Just for now, as best you can, allow them to be there. Your shoulders may drop and some tension may leave your body when you accept this feeling and fully allow it to be present. When I have a hard time with this, I imagine myself as the observer of this situation instead of the person reenacting it. I step out of myself and view myself with this problem.

Now, could you some way, even just a little bit, if you had to, just let this feeling go? Could it be possible drop it like a pen? Have you ever been able to let it go in the past? Could it be possible again? Would you be willing to drop it? When? Deep breath and…release.

That is it. Repeat this process as many times as necessary. Sometimes it comes quickly and sometimes it gets a little less painful with each process. Again, I strongly encourage you to get more involved with the Sedona Method and Hale's advancement of the work of an incredible gentleman by the name of Lester Levinson to get a deeper knowledge and appreciation of these release techniques. It is so simple and so powerful. To recap, think of the issue that creates tension. Allow it to be present and welcome it.

Could you let it go?

Would you let it go?

When?

This is a tool you can use quickly and silently whenever you are feeling a way that doesn't serve you well. It could be when you're craving certain foods or when you have the strong desire to emotionally eat or overeat. You can do this any time you feel stress or anxiety or any other thing, situation, or feeling you would like to let go of. You can use this quite literally for the excess fat on your body that you would like to release; as you release it, imagine it melting and falling away from your body. Create a visual image and hold it firm.

Releasing Stress

I'd like to share just a couple more thoughts on the subject of release. There were more than a couple of things along my journey that I had to release, personally. Some were big, emotional issues that stemmed way back, and some were more fleeting thoughts in the moment. It makes no difference; they can all be released. I've had to let go of anger and hurt from my from my parents not teaching me better eating habits when I was little, and all of the blame associated with that; but I've also had to release feelings that are much more shallow in thought, like the desire to eat something I knew wouldn't contribute to my perfect health or weight. Not everything has to be heavy duty.

I'll remind you again to stay aware of your feelings. They are your strongest connection between you and the universal mind. Shut them out, and you'll shut out your own divinity, block yourself from the self-love that you deserve, and perpetuate your current situation of poor health, because if you don't love yourself—or worse if you hate yourself—then it's only natural and expected that this would show up in your physical presence. I've always thought it odd that we can attribute getting in shape and achieving great health to a positive sense of being and loving ourselves, yet we judge some people harshly for feeling so good about who they are and how they feel about their body. Curiously, we have such a harder time acknowledging that the opposite is also true: that if we self-hate, we can end up manifesting sickness, disease, or obesity. It's true that what you think about you bring about. You can release thoughts, situations, or people who are not contributing to your personal growth and your positive desires. Only you can allow these things to be part of your physical experience and only you can attract them through your thoughts.

Stress is on top of the list of things that can cause us to over-eat and bring on an array of physical problems, even cancer and disease. Stress in all its forms can also be released, because it is only something we create inside ourselves, out of thin air. Remember, it takes more energy to create something than it takes to release it and likewise, if we can create it, we can re-lease it. Exercise is an excellent form of physical release, even just walking.

When I started my journey to good health, there were some very difficult moments in my life, some of the hardest I've ever had to deal with. This is the kind of stress that would have sent me into eating or drinking binges to avoid the pain, or at least distract myself from it. Fortunately, I was in a state of mind that was slightly stronger, and I released much of this tension with exercise, mostly walking. I've since integrated meditation and walking as outlets for release. No longer do I stuff my emotions deep inside and cover them over with layers of food. I've relearned healthier methods of coping that come naturally to me now, and I can do them anywhere.

I learned one technique that will physically release tension and stress as well as the desire to emotionally eat. This is a very simple yet very powerful technique. Close your eyes and sit if you can. Take a moment to get quiet. If you are feeling any tension or stress, allow those feelings to be present in your body. Welcome them to the best of your ability. That they are there, just for this moment, is OK. It's not your fault. They are just feelings you would like to release, and you will. Feel the tension that may exist in the solar plexus area near the center of your chest, and take a deep breath in while you press both hands together in front of you right at that point at chest level. Hold and press firmly while you focus on the stress of the tension that you feel. Slowly release the breath and your hands, and open them out as wide as you can reach. Feel the tension exit your body and repeat the words "I want to feel good" either to yourself or even better, out loud. It's simple and effective. Do this at least once a day, and you will start to experience sharp and vivid releases in your life.

By the way, this is still a beneficial technique even if you're not feeling stress at the moment. Release always feels good. We hide and suppress most of our stress so that we don't feel most of it most of the time. Men are especially effective at this. So release is good to do anytime. It makes you feel good, and there is nothing wrong with feeling good, regardless of what may have been drilled into your head up to this point.

I've also learned to take a calm, easy approach to life. I've learned to ask myself questions like "Will this situation matter in six months, one year, or five years from now?" The answer is almost always no. I've learned to make efforts to surrender my ego and realize that I don't have to win an argument to be right. It's not the winning that makes you right; it's the truth behind the words or feelings you have. I've learned that my feelings are always right and can't be argued with. I now realize that I can listen to these feelings and let them guide me, and if I don't like the way they make me feel, I can choose different thoughts and focus on how I do want to feel or what I do desire and make a shift right in that moment. I've learned to breathe and slow down and be deliberate and mindful in my life.

There is a great prayer, originally created by Reinhold Niebuhr, that has been adopted and modified by Alcoholics Anonymous and now reads,

SIX SIMPLE TRUTHS
. . . . . .

God, grant us the serenity to accept the things we
cannot change, the courage to change the things we can,
and the wisdom to know the difference.

Serenity, courage, and wisdom are at the backbone of your personal transformation. What you may not understand, and I surely did not when I started, is that you have all of these things in abundant and never-ending supply within you already. You are very much connected to this universal source. That is why this strength is abundant in you. This is a key idea; if you get nothing else, get this. You have all of this and more than you'll ever need right inside of you, always. It can never be taken away, even though at times when you needed it the most you may have ignored it or not been willing to see it. It was still there. It is there now.

You have all the serenity, all the courage, and all the wisdom you'll need for your journey through this life. You are special and you are unique and your life experience is important and was consciously chosen by you. You are beautiful, and you were intended to be here, the proof of which is that you are in fact here. And you are a piece of the universal perfection and balance from which we all originated. You could say that you are a piece of the universal intelligence, manifested into physical form. You've picked up some baggage along the way, true. You've added some padding as you've been banged around like a piece of luggage by a thrower, but you are whole. You don't need to go "out there" to find the answers. The answers are all inside of you. That is the nature of your heart's wisdom, and therefore your nature. It will surprise you with its knowledge if you allow it to be heard. You have courage beyond your conception, if you'll only release it and allow it to lead you instead of your intellect or your mind.

RELEASE

· · · · · ·

You have the serenity of the quietest and calmest pond in the still of the night stuck in time, if you'll only listen and allow that peace to be.

You see, you've started your journey with all these things in abundant supply. You can't lose them. You can't give too much away. In fact, the more you give, the more you get back. Sometimes you have everything you need, but yet you still look for the answers on the outside because you don't think you're good enough on the inside. Anything you see in another person that you like, you noticed because you have it inside of you, as well. It was "like attracting like" right before your eyes. You inner wisdom connected with it because that is your true nature, because we all came from the same source and have the same exact resources to draw from.

And you've only added things that get between you and this natural state. Your natural state is one of perfect health. You only need to take all the unnecessary things that have been added on (refer to your story) and one by one release them all. You see, it's all one big return trip to where you started. You've already been there. You already have all you need for this trip. You only need to get out of your own way and allow…

"Truth is what stands the test of experience." — *Albert Einstein*

ALLOW

Simple Truth 4
Things will flow to you when you get
out of your own way and allow.

MY FINGERS ARE tingling with excitement because we've already trekked across the most challenging part and are heading for some fun now. That's right. The hardest part is behind us now and we're gaining a head of steam. Allowing is where the magic happens, and it requires so little of you. This is the most passive part of life—allowing. To sum it up in five simple and easy words:

GET OUT OF THE WAY!

That's correct. Allowing is really just as simple as that. There are good things happening all around you every day, and there are beautiful people everywhere waiting for you to take their hands. There are great books, awesome and inspiring songs; there is the strength of millions of people right in front of you if you'll just tune in and listen. They were always there, but you just didn't always see them. You were sitting in the dark, and you only needed to turn some lights on and open the shades and let the light in. It was always trying to get in.

Once you do this, you will see more and more of the beauty and perfection in the world now that you are becoming more mindful and aware. You will have started releasing so much from your life by this point, so much that was unnecessarily clogging you up. In this release you'll have created a void—that's right—where those old habits, thoughts, and feelings used to take up space. The universe won't tolerate a void, so although it is very exciting place to be, it is also a very important place to put your mindful intention and attention. Whatever you do, as you've made it this far, please do not stop here. Keep going. You've worked through the painful parts, and it's time to reap the benefits now.

There is a void that will be filled with something. Let us consciously decide and choose what we'll allow to be there. Think of your soul like a dry sponge right now. You've just wrung out a bunch of old, dirty water that wasn't doing much good for you and your heart's desires. As you've released your grip on that sponge, new thoughts, ideas, habits, people, and things will come flooding into your life—and you get to design what that is going to look like. That's right, you do. In the past many of us have lived our lives in the default lane. We've allowed others to fill that space with whatever they wanted, or we've paid no conscious attention and received what came our way. Well, all that changes right now.

This is called living on the active side of life. It's what life is all about! It's about tuning in to your heart's desires and allowing those things to come to you. You don't have to do anything you don't want to do or hang out with people you don't care to or people who don't make you feel good. You owe it to yourself to find the people who do make you feel good. These people will help you on your path to fulfilling your heart's desires, only one of which is to be healthy. It is a beautiful moment in your life when you come to the realization through mindfulness that you don't have to allow thoughts that make you feel depressed or angry or bitter. In a single moment, you can release them and replace them with better, more productive thoughts.

So how do we actively design our lives? How do we become our lives' architects? Through a few simple and fun steps, we will make this process effortless. First, start by creating a list of things and people and situations you'd like to create. Please be open to possibility. Before you start, do a ten- or fifteen-minute meditation and get your mind and heart aligned and cleared of distractions. Go somewhere quiet where you will not be disturbed. Create a special environment for yourself. Light a candle if you like. Put on some soft and quiet meditation music. Release all distractions and tensions and worry that you may be having. Be prepared and willing to answer all of these questions with wholehearted honesty.

I sometimes tell people to describe someone else's life that you imagine being perfect. Many times people who have mastered suppression for years have a hard time envisioning themselves with this perfect life, but they can very easily see someone else's success or happiness. In fact, many of these same people have spent the better portion of their life supporting and helping other people. They have all the things they need to be happy, but it's a sad irony that they won't allow themselves to enjoy it.

So, just to get started, if you feel it would be helpful, imagine someone else's perfect life with the things you think would make it that way (we will make this your life). Get very clear. Go somewhere special, perhaps in nature where you can connect with your oneness and your connectedness with everything else, and describe in detail what the perfect life would look like in the following categories. Take notes and above all have fun. This, along with all the action you will take on your journey, is action that is intended to be fun. Your life's mission is to enjoy yourself while you are here. Your joy is your reason for being alive, so please allow this process to be fun. You don't have to share this with anyone until you are ready, and then only with those who will support you in this quest. Here we go:

Physical:

Describe your perfect body.

How much do you think you would weigh?

What do you feel like?

Describe your energy levels.

What size and kinds of clothes do you wear? What kind of shoes, glasses, contacts, or maybe you've gotten laser surgery to correct your eyesight?

Leave no details out and be as descriptive and visual as you can possibly be. Take very detailed notes.

Financial:

Describe your house, cars, and things.

How much money do you have in the bank?

How much is saved in your retirement accounts?

What would the world around you look like when you have complete financial stability?

A lack of money is a leading cause of stress and therefore obesity, so clarify any details that further describe your state of affairs when money is no longer a factor.

Career:

How do you spend your days?

What is it about your work that brings you joy, in your current job or a different one you would prefer?

How could you add special and unique value to the world with your gifts?

What is something you would do daily for free if the opportunity presented itself?

Remember, compensation comes in many different forms.

Relationships:

What kind of loving relationships do you see yourself in?

With your children?

With your spouse or significant other?

With your friends?

What do your new friendships look like?

How do you spend your time with all of these people?

How do you have fun with all of these people?

Recreation:

Where do you want to travel and what do you want to see to expand your view of the earth, your personal playground?

Whom do you want to see or meet?

What fun events and activities do you aspire to do?

There are no limits here. Really allow yourself to go wild.

Personal Growth:

What do you want to learn more about or become?

How do you want to better yourself (in any way)? Life is all about growth.

What do you feel would make you even better at giving your special gifts to the world?

What would make you a better teacher?

What new skills would you like to develop?

Community:

What would you like to give back to the community around you or on a larger scale (from the local PTA to the Red Cross)?

What group has done the most for you that you would like to do something for?

Whom could you help if you were at your ideal body weight and health? What would you help them with?

What could you contribute to your surrounding environment to make the world a better place?

Now that you have all these things written down, we'll move towards making this a clear visual image. Take all that you have written down in all of these areas and start a Top 100 list of all the things you would like to be, do, and have while you're in this physical body. You won't have to necessarily finish this list right away, as it will always be a bit of a work in progress. Feel free to cross things off that no longer appeal to you or add things that now excite you. Your life is a work in progress and you do not have to rigidly stick to something that you decided years ago. You are always free to change your direction and change your mind. Just be sure you're heading in a direction and experiencing the full richness of the life you intended when you came into physical being.

> *"A foolish consistency is the hobgoblin of little minds."*
> *— Ralph Waldo Emerson*

Keep this list somewhere you can refer to it often. Some of the things on this list may be very simple and you'll achieve them quickly. Some may take years to get to. No matter. You now have something to follow, a blueprint of sorts to guide you— one that you've created.

Visual Cues

So you've broken down your desires into seven categories and started your Top 100 things to do list. Great! I hope you're feeling some excitement. You are designing the life you were meant to live, and that should bring you incredible joy. This will really start to set in when you realize that you can actually be, do, or have any of those things with a lot more ease than you may currently think. To help bridge this gap between what you want and where you are, it's most helpful to have visual cues to bring you there. The more often you can see these cues, the more you will start to really connect with this vision. And please, don't worry if some things on your list seem too outlandish. If that is the case, then you did this exercise perfectly. There should be some things on there that will stretch you out.

ALLOW

· · · · · ·

If you can conceive it in your mind, it can be brought to life.

To find your visual cues, start looking for photos of as many of these things as you can find. Look online at Google Images or Photo Bucket or other great Web sites where you can find free images. Look in magazines, newspapers—anywhere you may see an image or even a quote or a word that speaks to you. Always be looking for images and words that you can add to your collection. Gather all of these pictures and phrases and photos together and get a large piece of poster board, foam board, corkboard, or cardboard, whatever you can get your hands on. The bigger it is, the better it will work. Your mind is limitless and does not prefer to work on small surfaces.

When I was writing this book I handwrote the first draft on large 14" x 17" lineless artist sketch paper so that my mind was not confined by space or lines. Really take the time to relax and get into state when you do this exercise, much like you did when you were preparing your list in your seven different categories. Set aside some time and some quiet space. For some, I suggest doing this exercise alone, as this is your dream, and though you will probably have people very close to you that would happily participate in this with you, people that you probably support every day, I really would like to see you do this for yourself, by yourself, without any outside influence. Sometimes we hold back when we involve other people in our dreams. Sometimes we think, even at a subconscious level, "Oh, they would think I'm unrealistic or judge me in some way or think I'm selfish if they saw all the things I wanted." Listen, you can only think for yourself, not for anyone else. No other person on the planet is going to design your perfect life for you the way you see it, so I suppose by definition, our very existence on this planet could be considered selfish by some.

You deserve it. The happier you are, the more you will have to give back. Go for yours. This is your life experience, not anyone else's. Protect your right to live it on your terms.

Paste or tape your pictures to make a big collage with all your dreams and visions on it. This is commonly referred to as a vision board; if you do a search online, you will find many ways to advance these techniques and use other media to make this vision even clearer and with more emotion. One thing I started doing was to turning my vision boards into videos. You can do so with Web sites like animoto.com, where you simply upload your different photos, write some text into blank spaces with motivational sayings or affirmations, and then upload your favorite inspirational song and the program will produce the whole thing for you. You can do as many of these as you like, as often as you like, and I encourage you to freshen them up and have several. You want them to all be constantly evolving, as you are constantly evolving, which is your nature and the nature of everything around you. To evolve, change, and grow. Stagnation is directly opposed to your true nature. View these videos and look at this vision board every day. Hang it up somewhere you can see and be proud of it. This is why you are alive: to experience these different things.

If this seems awkward to you, so be it. It's normal to feel like this, but you'll get used to it. Through this whole process, everything I'm teaching here is simple, easy, and fun. However, some of us are not used to doing for ourselves and taking care of ourselves first. You have to. It will make you a better worker, spouse, parent, grandparent, friend, sibling, lover, all the different roles you play in life. You have to take care of yourself first so that you can be the most you are capable of. It's only at that point that you will truly be able to give back all that you are capable of giving. Makes sense, right? The more you are, the more you can give. How much more could you give your loved ones if you were in perfect health? How much could you give them if you were to exit the planet prematurely due to poor health? I know this may sound grave, but this was the reality I was looking at square in the eyes when I was at my heaviest. Wherever you are in your journey or with your health, improvement will only serve to make everyone's life around you better. So embrace the "awkward" feeling, and if you start to feel guilt, acknowledge that guilt, allow it to be present, and calmly release it back out into the universe where it will dissipate. Guilt and stress, just like a virus, cannot survive outside of a host. Get it out of you, and it will evaporate. It is like a stray cat. It keeps coming back because you keep feeding it.

With regards to your vision board, have fun with this process and put some fun music on while you're creating this beautiful work of art. Some people tend to leave out fun when they are making plans for their lives, and then they wonder why they aren't having any fun. That's like if I really liked to have grilled barbeque chicken, but every time I went to make my grocery list, I never put the ingredients on it, then later complained that I never had barbeque chicken. If you don't put the ingredients for fun on your list, or even worse, don't have a list, it's highly unlikely that you'll run across a whole bunch of it. That would be like expecting barbeque chicken to magically appear in your life. Look, something will appear, so why not consciously choose it and mindfully design it as opposed to living in a default mode.

Watch your vision video and look at your vision board daily, and you will start to attract these things and situations into your life. It may seem unbelievable that it could be that simple at first. To be perfectly honest with you, I had my doubts when I did my first vision board…until it started to work. While this exercise will work better and more quickly if you believe and expect it to work, it doesn't rely on your belief to start working. It does require the action of taking the first step, however. Remember, the universe rewards action.

A Crash Course in Affirmations

Now that you have a visual, it's time to put all of these ever-so-powerful words that you use to work for you in a positive manner. Go through each of the seven categories and make an affirmative statement. Jack Canfield makes some excellent suggestions in *Success Principles* to keep your affirmations as effective and powerful as possible.

Try to keep the following guidelines in mind when designing your own affirmations. The most important thing to remember about a good affirmation is that it moves you emotionally and speaks to you, regardless of these guidelines. Remember, emotion is the magnet that will attract these things to your life experience.

1. Always state in the positive. Don't tell the universe what you don't want (more on this later). Always, always, always focus on what you want, not on what you don't want. As we've talked about before, what you think about expands, so if you're thinking about what you don't want, you'll get more of it. This lesson really took me a while to get. If I said, "I do not want black shoes," what image comes to mind? Black shoes. If I said, "I'm thankfully enjoying my new, clean and polished black leather wingtips shoes," what comes to mind? A very clear image. Always be clear with your intentions.

2. Always use the present tense. You need to be coming from a place of already having, not of wanting to get. This is why we must affirm in the present tense. For example:

(Effective) "I am joyfully driving my fully paid for, brand new, white convertible Porsche Caymen with taupe colored leather interior as I cruise through the mountains with the fresh wind in my hair."

(Not as effective) "I want a Porsche." Well, you may very well end up with a Porsche, but will it run? Will you like the color? Will you be able to afford it? You get the point.

Both are seemingly affirming the same thing, but one is coming from a placed of not having. The universe does not know of lack. It has plenty of everything. We humans don't always distribute it all out quite so evenly, but there is plenty out there when we live in harmony with the earth. When you come from a place of having it already, your mind (and your ego) will both be working feverishly, even while you sleep, to make it happen. You will be looking subconsciously for opportunities to get you closer to your affirmations and bridge the gap between your current reality and your vision so as to not have any inconsistencies in your story. Remember that story? Well, here it comes again, and you are currently rewriting it. Pretty cool, huh?

3. Have your affirmations contain and "ing" word. This will keep the thing you want coming from a position of already having it instead of wanting it, as well as add action and emotion, all at the same time. These three components together are like putting a rocket booster on your dreams.

4. Be specific. Please, don't leave any details out. Be as specific as you can. If you are talking about your physical body, you may want to include the size clothes you're wearing, size waist or other body measurements, body fat percentage (see hydrostatic body fat testing in appendix), or your exact weight, what you look like in the mirror, etc., and set an exact date when this will occur.

5. Contain a "feeling" word. Again, this will add emotion. Think of emotion like a hot sauce on your food (if you like hot sauce). It makes it much more powerful and therefore effective. It kicks it up a notch, as Emeril would say. Remember, these affirmations must be made real. You have to be able to feel them. The more they move you, the better they will work. With practice, I became so effective with my affirmations and visualizations that I could actually see the people that I was eventually helping. I could see you reading this book and transforming and living a more brilliant life, and it brought me to tears. Now that's real.

6. Keep the affirmations as short as you can while still being descriptive. The shorter, the better, so that they can be remembered. Granted, not all will be very short, but at least be sure you have some short ones in there for an "on the go" affirmation. Just be mindful that they don't all ramble on for a paragraph. It's a helpful tip to see if you can get some of them to rhyme like a jingle. That's why all great marketing efforts put their ideas to music with a jingle. It works. (example: I'm feeling alive and great at 178.)

7. Keep them personal. These affirmations will not work for others, just you. This is a simple yet constantly overlooked principle. You can't change other people, and you can't set your intention on them. You can create big problems when you do. They have to do it and want it for themselves when they're ready or it just doesn't stick, just like nobody else could get you to release weight until it was the right time for you and it was your decision. This, of course, does not mean that you can't encourage others or positively influence their thoughts. Start these affirmations with an "I am" to help you out here.

8. Always end your affirmation sessions with a "this or something better" statement. Your vision may be small compared to what the universe has in store for you, so leave some wiggle room for expansion here. You'll more than likely need it, especially until you start to get this muscle stronger and your vision expanded. Four weeks after doing my first vision board and affirmations, I had to completely revise the entire thing because I realized that my purpose was much deeper and vision much broader than I had first thought. That's OK. You have to have goals. Visualize them and affirm them, but they don't always turn out the way you saw them...often they're better.

Below are some of the affirmations I started with, though I do highly recommend you do further research on the subject. Shakti Gawain has a wonderful book by the name of *Creative Visualization* that I also recommend.

"I am mindful of what I put in my body."

"I assist and work with my body to help reach its natural and healthy state. I feed my body the highest quality foods and my diet is full of fruits and vegetables."

"I get immense pleasure from my exercise routines. I value the time I set aside for myself for exercise as my private time. I connect with my heart and achieve inner peace. This empowers me and makes me want to do more. The more I do, the better I feel, and so goes the upward spiral."

"Every day, all day, my body is rapidly moving toward its natural healthy state, even while I sleep."

"Physical activity releases stress and calms my mind. This better equips me for life."

"I am at my ideal weight already in my mind. My body is catching up with my mind more and more every day."

These affirmations perhaps weren't all perfect, but they worked. My affirmations have grown on many different levels since then, and I have made some of the most powerful affirmations for all different areas of your life available on my Web site for you to use at www.SixSimpleTruths.com. They are also recorded and available for immediate download if you would like to pick some of your favorites. The original affirmations that I used when I started are listed in the back of the book in the appendix.

ALLOW

· · · · · ·

One of the most powerful affirmations that I later come up with that led me to be inspired to write this book was simple yet so strong for me.

"I listen to and trust my heart."

You see, I know this one to be powerful because it was my heart's connection that picked me up when I didn't think I could keep going and gently brushed me off and gave me the wisdom I needed to continue. I look back on these affirmations today, after having read dozens and dozens of books on the subject and spoken at length for hours with some of the finest and most accomplished masters on the subject, and I see deep wisdom in the words I wrote at the very beginning before I intellectually understood any of this or why or how it worked. You too have that power right inside of you. Never feel as though you are not enough, not strong enough, smart enough, disciplined enough. You are! You have an abundance of wisdom and strength right inside of you because you are directly connected with source energy and it knows no lack of anything.

The real and full power of an affirmation comes when you draw a mental visual image in your mind and get very specific, like, "I see myself wearing pants with a thirty-four-inch waist. I have a pleasant profile and I am fit and flexible. I am quick and light. I am healthy and my health is sustainable." I still love this one and I do it every single day. Imagine what those pants look like. What color is the shirt? If I waved a magic wand and could put you instantly into that existence, how would it feel? Magical, right? Incredibly, overwhelmingly happy and vibrant, right?

Well, this is not too good to be true. This is exactly what you must do to make these visualizations most powerful and get them to work most effectively and quickly for you. The vivid visualization will enable you to feel the emotion you would feel when you have the thing you are visualizing. It is this emotional energy that gives the visualization and affirmation the fuel to take off into the universe and return to you in physical form. You do not want to just say the affirmation in a disbelieving way and move on to the next one. Get into it. Really let yourself go for it and experience the thing you want right now, in your mind, in your heart. It only takes a couple of minutes a day.

OK, so how do you get yourself to do this every day? I'm glad you asked because I've developed a way to make even your affirmations seem effortless. If you go to my Web site, www.SixSimpleTruths.com, and click on Affirmations, there is an entire section where you can download affirmations. I have recorded and set to meditation music different affirmations for each day of the week so they won't get stale or start to feel overused. Simply download them onto your mp3 player and a couple of clicks later you'll have them ready to listen to every day. If you have created an affirmation that you think will be helpful to others, please share it on the site.

These affirmations are one of the first steps to allowing all the good to enter your life. They put pictures, numbers, people, and places in the void you've created through your releasing work. This is all part of starting to love and take care of yourself and to allow yourself to have the things you deserve, including but not limited to, not in any way, a new slim and fit body. You can always go to www.SixSimpleTruths.com and look at before and after pictures and videos and read inspirational stories to realize many other folks have traversed the same ground as you and had fabulous and effortless results.

This is all part of you creating an encouraging and supportive environment for yourself. When you surround yourself with people who see you as you really are—whole, complete, and perfectly aligned with your true nature—you will more quickly attract your vision to your experience.

I recommend doing your affirmations and visualizations at specific times. I do this so that we don't forget to do them. I think of it as a maintenance type of activity for my soul. It is all too easy to forget to do this, so having a scheduled time to play your affirmations or do your visualizations will really help you to follow through. I have found that at night before you go to bed and in the mornings before you wake up are excellent times. The evenings help you bring closure to a beautiful day for which you are grateful, and the mornings help you start the day off on the right note and set the tone for the remainder of your day. This is powerful, and I suggest you try to work with this guideline.

I also want to point out a very important point. Affirmations and visualizations are at their most powerful when you are already in your "zone," when you are feeling most connected, most inspired, most excited about whatever it is that you are doing. This is when they are most believable to your mind and when they actually have the largest and most powerful impact on your life. Think of this as riding a really good wave. When you are on it, you want it to last as long as possible and get the most fun out of it. It is at this time that you may want to try out some new affirmations or tackle some that you may have been reserved about doing in the past. Practicing your affirmations while in this state will yield you results many times greater than when you are not as inspired or when you are feeling down.

Does this mean you shouldn't do your affirmations when you are feeling down? Absolutely not! This is also a very, very important time to do them but for different reasons. These affirmations that I created were designed to help get me out of a slump, move me into my zone, and then keep me there. There were and are many days where I wake up uninspired to get out there and do the things I know I must do, and these affirmations help re-center me and remind me of what I already know and believe. I think it is very powerful to hear these words coming daily to reaffirm the thoughts or ideas.

So you see, it is also very important to listen when you are at your worst. I know that this one tool alone, which is free for you to use, can be the deciding factor in your ultimate failure or success, if only you apply it daily. And let's face it; it is pretty easy to hit the play button, even when you're not feeling so good. I'm trying to weed out all of the possible excuses that your ego may come up with to empower you to seize your success for yourself. And while it is important to listen while you're down, it is powerful, for different reasons, to also listen while you are at your best. Make sense? Good, now pay attention to this next part. It is arguably the most important concept in the book, and I find that I relearn this concept every day and get a little deeper in it. The trick to having is being.

Be, Do, Have

Affirmations will get you in the right state of mind to make you start *being* the person you really are. As I've said, you don't need to change anything about who you already are, your true nature. It came with divine perfection. It is just fine. It's all of the extra junk that has been added over the years that needs to be released and the void filled with these new visions and affirmations. In fact, it is only after you have released these unnecessary additions that you will really get to know the real you. And this process is a never-ending one. You will constantly surprise yourself with what you are capable of and with the levels of compassion and wisdom that reside within you. Yes, already within you.

When you do, you will start seeing yourself like the person in your visions. You will become more and more like that vision every day. You will start doing things that the slim and fit person would do, and those actions will lead you to the things that person would naturally have. This is the whole BE, DO, HAVE principle you may have heard of in the past. Sounds simple, right? Sure, everyone knows that, right?

Well, not exactly. Most people all too often look for the answers "out there." They think if they "have" first, then they will do the right things and end up being the person they wanted to be. Most people are convinced that money will bring pure joy to their lives; otherwise why would we spend so much time trying to accumulate it while at the same time trading our time with our loved ones for more of it. If having worked that way and first brought about the true, lasting satisfaction we yearn for, whenever someone hit the lottery their lives would be instantly and forever happy. Is that the case? No, of course that is far from the truth, and the reality of the statistics tells another story. When you go about this in the reverse order, it defies the simple truth of allowing and the equation doesn't balance. This is where the majority of the world is getting stuck, not only with their weight and health, but also with relationships, finances, and overall happiness.

Another brilliant and relevant example of this is when people think they need to have a new diet regimen, gym membership, or new workout equipment in order to start doing the things they need to do in order to be the healthy person they desire to be. As we all know and many of us have experienced, the diet goes in the trash can under the Doritos bag, the gym membership card gathers mold in your gym bag, and the exercise equipment eventually ends up on Craigslist (a great place to purchase equipment, by the way), right? Right, because in these scenarios you have chosen to change from the outside hoping it will come in. This formula assumes the answers need to be found outside of you and that implies that you are not enough to be complete as is. As long as you buy into this way of thinking, again, your equation won't balance out. Think of it like an algebra equation; put the x in the wrong spot and you won't get the right answer (and my high school algebra teacher thought I didn't get any of what she was teaching).

This is why the traditional approaches don't work. It is by becoming mindful of this and allowing a new way to enter your life that the ideas in this book will work, permanently and effectively and quickly if you allow. Start the healing inside and you'll realize you have everything you need. When you truly get this, you'll know you can start being that healthy person right now. Though you may not look like that person, things are not always as they appear. As you release you will start to physically transform back to your true nature, and then you will start doing things that align with this new being's "story" and vision. Only then will you have the things you so desire. Also remember, permanent physical transformation comes after emotional transformation. When you've connected with the true nature inside you, physical transformation will just naturally follow.

Got it? Simple, easy and fun.

1. BE like the person you aspire to be.
2. DO the things that person would do.
3. HAVE the things that person would have, not the other way around.

Just remember, your body wants to be healthy. It does not want to be overweight. When you start releasing fat, you start feeling better, more vibrant, clearer; and this will serve as confirmation and evidence of this fact I'm telling you. This is your body screaming, "YES! This is what I wanted, thank you!" This feeling good is what normal, natural, and right feels like. Right now you may be a little numb, a little zoned out to this, but just like a small baby, your vision will get better and better and better. So please, as you pass through this book, go back and reread chapters and you will hit new levels of understanding. You will see new colors on the page you didn't see before. I promise it. These are all signs of your heart opening up and you allowing yourself to return to your natural state.

The people, things, and resources you need to get to where your vision will take you will all appear as you allow. They were there all along. They are all there right now waiting for you. When you allow, they can then step onto your stage of your production where you call the shots. You do the directing, casting, producing, and you write the story. If you don't like how it's turned out so far, change it.

So by now you understand, at some level, how to employ gratitude into your daily life so that you can be in a place more open to receive the good you deserve and desire. You've learned the power of a focused mind and what can be accomplished with awareness and the catalyst of change that it can be. You've also been shown the simplicity of release to let go of the things that aren't moving you towards your heart's desires, followed by the beautiful art of allowing yourself to get out of the way and attract the right people and events and things right into your personal life.

You're getting along down the path now and learning new things every day. Get used to it, because as far as I can tell, that never stops. The universe will continue to bless you with wisdom and knowledge, and there is only one way to be sure you don't cut off this supply. It is the great Law of Reciprocity that keeps things moving round and round...

"Truth will always be truth, regardless of lack of understanding, disbelief, or ignorance."
— *W. Clement Stone*

GIVE IT AWAY

Simple Truth 5
The natural flow of energy works
only when we circulate it.

THE HEAVENS GIVE forth a vast abundance of water because
it is allowed to circulate. The oxygen we breathe is plentiful
because the earth readily gives it back and cleanses it. These
systems of circulation don't require more and more elements
as time goes by, even with an added load on what is being
used. There is just as much water now as there was a million
years ago. There is plenty to go around only because it is being
circulated, used, benefited from, and passed on. Where would
we be if the trees kept their water and never let it go, along
with the precious oxygen we need to live? Circulation and giving back is the way of the universe. It is why everything that is
good and life giving remains in existence.

It has been said that the only way to truly keep something
close and dear to you is to give it away. This is because of the
Law of Reciprocity. If we look at a broken economy, we will see
a shining example of this law in effect. With money, we can

easily see this. If everyone has money, where did they get it from? It was obtained through other people, of course, or businesses or institutions of some kind, all made possible through people. If everyone stops spending money, where does it go? It locks up and freezes the economy or the monetary environment. When this circulation slows down or stops, people stop receiving more. They get fearful and stop spending, which makes the problem worse. Keep this up long enough, and eventually the money itself becomes worthless.

But somehow we as a society tend to shun the idea that thoughts and goodwill operate under the same laws. Think of the gifts you have been given as perishable, but as long as you keep passing them along, they receive new, fresh energy with each new contact. Through this giving, a vacuum is created and more good will naturally be attracted to you. You can never give away too much of the good that is in your heart. You are connected to an endless supply, so it would serve you well to let go and release the thinking that you won't have enough.

When you have become aware and successfully been following these simple truths for an extended period of time, new insights and knowledge will come to you. They always do, always will, if you are open to receive. You will receive more insight through others sharing and circulating what they have learned. We are in an exciting time where information and knowledge is being spread so quickly and we are therefore growing and expanding at an incredible rate. Our overall enlightenment as a people is rapidly increasing; these new insights lead to a more fulfilling life, one where you can have the things you desire, including great health, more easily through your understanding of how it all works together. The Law of

Reciprocity states that you will get back equal or greater than what you put in. When you give something you have to another, you have created value where there previously was none. In turn you have raised the energy level of the person you extended the help to, and they go on about their day giving off a higher level of energy, thus improving the lives of others. This will be compensated by the universe. (That is the Law of Compensation, to which there are also no exceptions.)

Some people refer to this as Karma (a little different, but same concept), some say what goes around comes around, some say you get what you give. However it has been said, no doubt this concept should sound familiar to you and no doubt you've experienced it. In fact, you experience it every day, just like you experience gravity. Your lack of knowledge of it does not reduce its effects on you, as is true with all of the laws we operate under. It just depends on what you're putting out there as to what you're getting back.

The beauty of giving back is that anyone can do it. You don't have to, and shouldn't, wait until you've reached the end of your journey or until after you've released all of your excess weight. If you wait until the end of your journey, it will be too late. Game over. And the problem with waiting until you've accomplished your goals is that you will find your goals are constantly changing and growing; it's a process that never ends. It is this giving back that fuels your growth. These first steps I may have taken in the name of fat release, but that was only the beginning for me. They were only the first steps of many. They were my ticket to get in, and for that I am eternally grateful.

If you go to the beginning of this book you will find my vision statement. You will also find it on my Web site.

"My vision is to help people create an environment where a satisfied mind can prevail; where the pain and sickness of obesity are replaced with joy and passion so they too can freely give the world their special and unique gifts and through such action enable a global shift in consciousness thereby bringing light where there previously was darkness."

You may read this and think it's too ambitious. Good. A vision worth having should be as big as the heart that holds it. The bigger the vision, the bigger the people you will attract. Some others may look at that statement, nod their heads, and give a resounding, "Right on!" Still others, having felt the pain and experienced what life can be like with it removed, will feel it in their hearts to take action and help move the cause. You get to decide which you will be.

The change starts from within yourself and moves outward from there. These simple truths have always been there. They were there before the beginning of time and they will be there when this current physical presence is gone. They will stand up to any level of scrutiny because they are true. You can rest your confidence in them. Denying or ignoring their existence is much like denying or ignoring gravity. It doesn't change its effects on you.

All the great teachers have taught the same things in different ways. You only need to decide and figure out what your special and unique gifts are and figure out how to better the world with them while having fun and experiencing unbridled ecstasy. You see, I know what the darkness feels like when you can't get up the motivation to get off the couch, much less to help someone else. I know what it feels like to feel helpless and hopeless; and I know that in that state, I wasn't offering too much of anything to anyone.

Now I know in my heart that if I can help you leave that place so you never have to return, you will not only feel able to help your fellow man in some way, you will feel moved and compelled much like I feel moved to put these words on paper and get to the tallest mountain and shout them from the top of my lungs (though I've experienced better results with the Internet). I know what that kind of change can do to you, and I can't wait to see what beauty comes out of you when you decide that it's time to let it out. I trust you'll let me know about it.

Much like gratitude, it starts with the smallest thing. Lend a hand. Give a word of encouragement. The most powerful things don't cost money. They cost your attention and your energy, even just the energy of a thought or a kind word, even when you think it doesn't matter.

"Take Care of Each Other"

I was once walking around the indoor track at my local YMCA, alone. I often use this time to listen to audio books or music, to think, or sometimes just to be. These days I move at a pretty good pace compared to when I started. It's an upstairs track, and as I made the turn I saw this older lady grabbing the railing and pulling herself up the stairs. She made it to the top, a little out of breath, and very slowly started walking around the 1/17-mile elevated track. I must have passed her fifteen times as she stopped and went again, sometimes bent over in an attempt to catch her breath and recover some energy. I think she went around one time, and then she headed back down the stairs, slowly.

I passed the stairs, stopped and turned back, stuck my head over the railing, and said, "Hey." She looked up, a little shocked, almost as though she had done something wrong. I continued, "You did a great job! Keep it up and come back real soon." She smiled ear-to-ear and teared up. Her posture straightened, her head picked up, and she marched out of that gymnasium with more energy than she had when she nearly crawled in.

All I could think of was that this was someone's mother, probably someone's grandmother, could have been my mother or yours. She might have never set foot in a gym before that moment. I'd been there hundreds of times and had never seen her before. Who knows how much that little gesture, which cost me nothing other than a second and a breath, could have impacted her health or happiness for the better? I do know I've seen her many times since, and her pace and health have improved. This is only one small example of how you can improve the quality of someone else's life while at the same time your own. This is the Law of Reciprocity in action. It's easy, which is how it's supposed to be. All of life can become this easy if you allow and have a giving spirit. It takes so little to give the most valuable gifts to another, being but it means so much. This is leveraging your goodwill.

My great grandmother, who passed when I was only five, used to say, "Take care of each other." You know, most of the time, it requires so little of us to give back something to someone else, but so many times we keep it all to ourselves. That is not how we were created. That is not how our universe thrives. We were meant to give and give freely. It's in that giving that we receive the greatest and richest rewards we'll ever receive, rewards that far outweigh anything monetary wealth could ever create. I might not have completely believed that several years ago, but I couldn't be convinced otherwise now because I have a knowing within.

There are so many different ways to give back to the world around us. There are far more ways than there are people on the planet, so you'll never run out of ways to give back. Giving back brings you full circle to gratitude because you give back out of the gratitude for what you have been giving, and this in turn circulates the good feeling and good intent in the world.

Yes, the ways are abundant and endless. You do not have to wait for your transformation to be complete. In fact, I encourage you to start *before* your transformation is complete. This will speed up the process for you and align yourself with your true nature, which is one of giving. When you give you will attract the same vibrational energy right back to you. This is the Law of Attraction in play. When that energy comes back to you, you feel good and want to do more.

It works exactly the same with a negative thought or intention, which is why you want to monitor those thoughts and feelings. Please remember this, if nothing else from what you've learned here: your thoughts and words are more powerful than you may realize. In fact, they are the most powerful things in the world, for everything that is brought about by humanity is born from a thought.

When you have the body and mind that you have craved for so long but have not known how to get it until now, you will have the most incredible and powerful gift to give the world. Believe me, people will ask you, over and over again, "How did you lose the weight?" You will have endless opportunities to spread the word and describe the effortless process. You will tell them enthusiastically how it works and how their thoughts and visualizations become reality and how tying strong emotions to everything they think about speeds up the process. You'll tell them about how to connect to their inner self, their heart's wisdom, and get answers to any questions they have. You'll tell them they have everything they need right inside them right now. They will know you speak the truth because the truth has a ring to it that cannot be ignored or avoided; it sells itself.

Plus, you will be a living example of what you speak of. You will bring a new sense of hope and inspiration to all those you come in contact with, your friends, family, and coworkers. You will find ways to give back to your community, schools, children, and the earth. You will see the importance of taking care of our planet, just like you now take care of yourself. You will realize we are all connected and that you can't help yourself without helping another just as you can't hurt yourself without hurting another.

This keen sense of awareness you will have developed will flow into other areas of your life and you will no longer be able to ignore things that you used to. When you are deeply connected and listening to your heart, your desires will shift to those around you. You will make an incredible difference. This is why Ghandi said, "Be the change you wish to see in the world." He understood that if you were in touch with your true nature, the change would flow out of you and into the world and bubble over with abundance.

You cannot put your intention on another person, but you can hold those in need of help in a vision of happiness and joy instead of seeing them as they currently are. You can help them attract to themselves that which they desire, which is joy and happiness. It's what we all want, from the strongest to the weakest, from the most popular to the unknown, any race, color, religion; it's all the same deep within our true nature, a desire to be happy. Happiness is the gift you can give to the world. You can help people free themselves from the shackles of their own thoughts. A deep and satisfying peace waits there.

You don't have to "know" where to start. Like I've said before, the answers are all inside of you, all in your heart, and they will be revealed to you when you are ready. You don't have to know where you need to be in a year; you just need to get quiet and ask your heart where you need to be right now.

Now. Now is the only moment in your life that will ever matter. All you will ever do in your lifetime will be done in the moment we call now. You can't move back in time, and the future has not happened, but you will always have the present moment, for it is the only one your life exists in. So start small, that's OK, but do start. You can enter this glorious realm of giving anytime or anywhere you happen to be. Your current state of health has nothing to do with your ability to give on a daily basis and it has nothing to do with your health in the future, only that it was a place you once stopped, like a connecting flight to your desired destination.

As you grow and find your strength within, the things that seemed so hard in the beginning will seem effortless, and your ability and capacity to give will grow. It may be giving the gift of health to another or it may be giving a piece of you in another way. We all have something special that connects us to our world. We all have unique talents and gifts, but too many of us are hiding them, suppressing them, and the net effect of this manifests in our physical and emotional health.

I was hiding behind my veil of insulation. It wasn't until I started the process of release that my purpose came into sharp and clear focus. Yours will come, too, if you stay aware of it, if you're looking for it, if you allow it to flow into your life. All the tools you need you will have, and all the people required are already waiting for you; they will appear at just the right moment just as this book appeared in your life at just the right moment. You only need to trust that your heart, your inner being, can take you there. Whether your deeds of giving back are small or large makes no difference. You will have set forth a chain of new and exciting events that will take you further in your journey. You will have created a momentum that is unstoppable. You will have started attracting a new reality, a new way of life, and the old you will be a distant memory, a necessary one where you gathered experiences and lessons that you can now share with those you now help. Indeed, it was all part of the perfect and balanced universal and divine plan.

"A happy life consists not in the absence but in the mastery of hardships." — *Helen Keller*

Remember that the challenges on the road ahead are there for your benefit. Every person you come in contact with is there to teach you something, so be mindful of the lesson. You will learn to harness adversity and use it as a sail to move your vessel in the intended and desired direction. It is through hardships that you are given the opportunity to grow. When you can truly appreciate this contrast between that which you desire and that which you are experiencing and be grateful for what it truly is, an opportunity to move you down your intended path, even your less-than-joyful days will become something to look forward to and be grateful for. Isn't that a better way to view life?

There's one great secret to achieving what you want. It is this: when you can travel down the road less traveled, on the path of least resistance, and get to a point where what you seek you actually want for another person even more than you want it for yourself, that is when getting the thing you desire will be the only possible outcome for you. When you can get to a place where you desire to help others on their fitness journey and show them what you have learned, when this becomes a burning desire for you, this is a powerful indicator that you are there. I have witnessed this many, many times with people I have met who have released excess weight and went on to teach others how to accomplish this. This is the ultimate in serving as it pertains to that which you desire, better health. Your wanting this goodness for others even more than yourself is a great indication that you are irreversibly going the right way. Indeed, you will reach a point where going back is just not an option for you, and when you realize you are there, it will be a powerful moment for you. It is likely that you will, at that time, be working toward helping others do the same. This is the powerful secret I speak of, wanting it for someone else more than you even desired it for yourself. You see, we are all connected and you cannot help another without helping yourself. When you view the world this way you no longer are just a lonely island in the middle of the ocean but a part of a beautiful planet with great diversity and super connectedness. We all depend on each other, and it is in the helping of another that we reap the greatest benefits for ourselves. It is stepping outside of the self, the part, and taking care of others, the whole.

The more focused you keep your intention and the more

emotions you feel when doing your affirmations and visualizations, the more real you can create the image in your mind and the more speed you will move with toward your intended reality. Just be sure when you get there, and you will, that you take the time to be aware of your successes. Too often in this life, we get so engaged in the pursuit of happiness that we forget to enjoy the actual happiness, which is found in the pursuit, which of course is the object of our desire. There is opportunity every day to experience this happiness. You need only to close your eyes, crack a smile, and breathe deeply to feel this joy and then spread it out through the world.

With a base knowledge of the first five simple truths, you are now ready to start putting the pieces together and figure out where to place that first step.

Smile…take a deep breath…relax. This is the fun part. This is where it all happens. Life is seized in a moment of action.

"No man thoroughly understands a truth until he has contended against it." — *Ralph Waldo Emerson*

• • • • • •

APPLY

Simple Truth 6
Only applied wisdom can change
the intention into reality.

"Talk doesn't cook rice." — *ancient Chinese proverb*

WE'RE GETTING READY to cook some rice (brown rice, of course), so get ready for the changes to begin! Change is something that many people tend to fear, so if that is the case for you, take a moment and slowly release that fear right now, right in this moment. Say the following affirmations out loud and any time that you feel a fear of change:

I understand my personal growth comes through change.
I am joyfully embracing and welcoming change into my life.
Change is growth. Growth is good.

Change is inevitable. Change is why we're here. Without change, none of us would exist. Embrace it and its life-giving qualities. I've created a way to move forward that is so gradual you'll hardly know you've changed anything. By the time you've made the significant changes, you'll be in a different state of mind and much more connected with your true self. You'll remember your true self will always gravitate towards good health, so it actually becomes easier and easier to make the decisions that will bring you closer to your desires, and you'll be less likely to make the decisions that lead you away. This beauty and perfection, which is prebuilt into each and every one of us, is the source of the effortless ease.

Before we go any further, now that you have a basic understanding of the Six Simple Truths and how they work together, I would ask you to firmly set your intentions. This will be something you can refer back to. This will be your first step in applying the knowledge you have. There is strength and power to be received by following through on this action. It's easy, so don't think about it too hard—just jump in there and do it. Send these Six Intentions to intentions@SixSimpleTruths.com. Be sure to write in your name and put feeling into the action while you take this first step. This one movement can alter your life.

"Nothing happens until something moves." — *Albert Einstein*

You will feel a sense of empowerment flow to you once you have sent this off. Remember that feeling and keep this list of intentions somewhere you can see them every day. Hold them in your hands and read them aloud. This is what empowerment feels like. Get used to it. It will set you free. You can download a small, wallet-size print out of these intentions for free at my Web site at www.SixSimpleTruths.com by clicking on Downloads. You can also generate this e-mail directly from that page. You see, I've kept my commitment and made it easy for you.

I, _____, am clearly setting my
intention on how I choose to live my life from this day forward.

1. It is my intention to start every day in a spirit of gratitude for what I have.

2. It is my intention to carefully pay attention to my thoughts and emotions by taking deliberate action and reserving time to quiet my mind, daily.

3. It is my intention to let go of all thoughts that do not move me in the direction of my heart's desires.

4. It is my intention to allow all the good, right, and perfect people, things, and situations into my life experience.

5. It is my intention to circulate the good that I attract to my life.

6. It is my intention to diligently apply my heart's wisdom in my daily activities.

I understand that I am improving every day and that my love and acceptance of myself is unconditional and not dependent on my actions on any given day. I hold these intentions firm and send them out to the universe with love so that I may align my perfect health and life with my true nature.

. . . .

When I started my journey, as I have explained, I made something of a pact, a promise that I would earnestly move forward and trust in the process, even though I wasn't sure what the process was going to look like, and give it a chance to work. My only guideline or agreement with myself was that it was going to be easy. I've carried forth this ideal and this promise to this very day with myself. I will not force myself to do anything that

I feel resistance about. I either release the resistance and move forward effortlessly, or I just don't do it. It's that simple.

Everything in my life has to be sustainable. I no longer force myself through brutal workouts or agonizing fits of cardio torture to try to get an intended result. This is an important concept to get. That itself would be resistance. Resistance will always be met with resistance, and then when you encounter the first moment of weakness in your mental fortitude you'll fold like a cheap beach chair. Believe me, if I had had to release all the fat I did with nothing but willpower, I'd be heavier now than I was then. My body would have just patiently waited until I was finished with my little game and then whacked me hard on its climb back up to my previous weight plus a little. Ever happen to you before?

There is nothing wrong with grueling workouts or running marathons, if done properly and safely. I enjoy lifting weights with intensity. I'm talking about *making* myself do things that I don't want to or that I have no intention of sustaining in the long term. This, in my experience, always led me to resistance and resentment and ultimately failure. So be as intense as you want to be, but use caution when making yourself do something in the name of permanent fat release. Sustainability is what has eluded you thus far. So, to get a different result, it only makes sense that you'll have to try some different approaches.

You're going to take it slow and gradual. You're going to relearn how to eat and how to sleep and how to think, slowly. And don't be concerned with the timelines. How long it takes you is about as important as how long it took you to get in this shape in the first place. It's completely insignificant. One thing is in the past, and the other, in the future; the only moment you can do anything about is happening right now. The process is gradual, but that didn't stop me from releasing almost one hundred pounds in the first twelve months! That was plenty fast for me, and I'd caution you to be careful not to go too much faster than that. Notice I said to be careful, not necessarily blacklist it. Different people depending on their current weight and health will move at different speeds.

Be sure before you begin that you have typed out the Six Intentions and e-mailed them in. There is strength and power in asserting your intention and sending it out into the universe. It's the first step in a long chain of events that will change your life and the lives of many others, forever. Again, send your Six Intentions to intentions@SixSimpleTruths.com.

Think of this like an algebra class. Before you move on to a new concept, you want to be sure to grasp the previous one so that midsemester you aren't throwing textbooks across your bedroom and jamming pencils in the wall (OK, maybe that was just me). So take it slow. I may suggest a pace, but realize you can spend as much time in each phase as you feel you need to. This is your life, your body, and you call the shots. You are in control. The most important principle in applying this wisdom builds off of that idea.

Add, don't subtract.

Although you are a perfect being who was complete and whole the moment you were intended on this planet, and although you need to add nothing to yourself but only to release what is unnecessary, this first principle has to do with food, not with your beautiful soul. Remember, you and hunger are separate. You and food are separate. So start off this process with the adding principle.

SIX SIMPLE TRUTHS

• • • • • •

I began my journey, my easy journey, telling myself that I was not going to remove anything from my diet that I didn't want to. That meant if I wanted chips, pizza, wings, beer, you name it, it was on the menu. At the time, I felt as though I needed this food, so I wasn't mentally or emotionally ready to part with it. For it to be easy, I would only be able to add things, not take anything away.

Think of this technique like a cup of dirty water. Your eating habits being the unwanted particles mucking up the water. If you continue to pour good, clean water into this glass for a long enough period of time, you'll eventually have clean water. You'll never have had to go through the painful and shocking process of dumping out your glass altogether, because this would equate to loss in your subconscious mind. We tend to cling to our dirty water because it's the only water we think we have access to. Its safe. Its what we're used to and it's a better idea to work with that than to fight it. I've tried the other way around and it has always ended in reverting back to where I started. Again, for a different result use a different approach.

You see, we hang on to the fat we have because it protects us in some way. It stops us from achieving what we were intended here to achieve. It perhaps stops us from receiving and giving the full depth of love that we deserve in relationships. It holds us back, but make no mistake about it: we are getting something in return for this fat-keeping behavior. There is always some benefit, and it usually serves to protect us in some way. In my experience it's usually by keeping us from fully engaging ourselves in life, which I believe to be the single biggest misuse of our physical presence here on this earth. But whatever the reasons you may have, either obvious or not so much, they are serving you in some dysfunctional way. Letting these reasons and benefits go quickly and suddenly can be not only scary but also painful and shocking, much like dropping a fish from a cold bowl of water to a warm one. The shock alone can send you packing.

For me it was more like dropping the fish on the counter and watching him flop around. Believe me, I'm all about change and had searched my whole life for every conceivable way to change. I bought an endless number of programs and went to coaches and experts, and nothing worked in the long term. It wasn't until this time around, as I listened to my heart, my true nature, that it all just clicked. It's like a lock; so long as you dial in the right combination, it will open, every time, guaranteed, no exceptions, no matter who you are, where you're from, or what your life experiences have been.

So I'm all about you changing, but not at the cost of losing you to the 95 percent of the people who not only fail in an attempt to lose weight but gain some additional back. I don't want you to be that fish out of water. I know the courage and strength it takes to get up one more time and try again to address your weight issue. I respect you for coming back, and I promise you an easy and doable approach. We will not lose you to the diet vortex, so we will not stir up feelings of loss. This is why I've always referred to this as release, not as a loss. So, we add, not subtract, from the things you eat.

Ten Easy Steps

I've broken this down into simple, easy steps so you can add good into your life at your own pace. Please keep in mind that on average, I implemented about one step per week, so this process took me between three and four months. You may be able to do it faster than that, or you may find you need more time with each step. Go at your own pace and be patient. The speed of the pace is not what is important. Movement in the right direction is.

Step 1: Add the habit of daily gratitude.
The habit of daily gratitude is a huge part of adding good to your life. I want to revisit the first simple truth about gratitude. Every morning upon waking, think of three things you are grateful for and thank the universe for allowing you to enjoy these things. Follow that up with this statement:

> **I am open to receive all of the beautiful gifts and abundance the universe has for me, today and every day. Thank you for another wonderful day.**

This may seem trivial. You may even have the inclination to skip this step. Please do not. This may seem a little awkward in the beginning, or even strange, like trying to throw a ball with your non-dominant arm, but do it. It's a great way to start every day. So regardless of how it makes you feel at first, start every morning this way, even when you're sick or depressed, especially on those mornings. If you find yourself in the middle or at the end of a day and realize that you have forgotten, it's never too late to be grateful.

Step 2: Add 64 ounces of water per day.
At this point, it's time to start adding water, the queen in this chess game. None of this would be possible without an adequate supply of water. It serves so many purposes, but for now, all you need to realize is your body is mostly composed of it,

and if you want to release the fat and toxins, you've just got to be drinking water, a minimum of 64 ounces per day. It's good to drink more if you can, and you'll probably see quicker and more effective results if you do, but let's remember my promise of ease. I have failed on past diets because I couldn't keep up with the water consumption required. As soon as I messed up on something like this, I threw the whole thing out the window. Sixty-four ounces is an easy amount to stick. For me that meant never leaving home without my thirty-two-ounce water bottle (get two if you have to).

One great thing water did for me, other than hydrate me, was to turn off about 30 percent of my hunger signals, which were actually thirst signals I interpreted as hunger. Once again, my food intake went down again voluntarily. These days it's something I'm still mindful of when hunger creeps up on me. The first thing I ask myself is "Have I had enough water?" An extra glass never hurts, so when I'm feeling hungry, even if I do intend to eat, I'll always drink a nice big glass of water first. I think of this as a speed bump to slow me down a bit. Every time you feel hunger, this should be a prompt to have a drink (of water, not booze). It is extremely effective, so don't leave home without your water bottle, and know you can always drink more.

Step 3: Add one piece of fruit every day.
When it comes to food, start by eating one piece of fruit every day. An apple, orange, or berries—right now it really doesn't matter what kind. Try to mix it up as much as possible and get as much variety in as you can. The ideal time to do this is in between meals. When you find yourself getting hungry, eat a piece of fruit. Our bodies are so starved for nutrients that the simple act of eating some good, live nutrients like those found in fruits

and vegetables can immediately begin to turn things around.

There's a great book out by Jon Gabriel called *The Gabriel Method*. He theorizes that your body has so-called internal "fat programs" that tell your body to store fat just like a computer program running in your body. Eating good, nutrient-based, live foods along with implementation of some other good habits can turn these programs off. I found it to be one of the better books available on the subject of fat release, especially because Jon had experienced severe obesity himself. He didn't learn these things in a laboratory or in a college classroom. Jon, like me, like you, experienced the pain. It is in this common likeness that we can speak to you and feel your pain. It has been said that a teacher can only be as effective as their understanding of where their student is, and I believe that is part of the reason these truths will work for you. It is uniquely authentic and there is a reason it rings true to you. Trust that and follow it. It is your heart telling you that you are on the right path.

Step 4: Add one vegetable every day.

Once you're comfortable with one piece of fruit daily and you're ready to try something a little more intense, add a vegetable every day. I know, crazy, right? Again, I suggest varying the vegetable as much as possible. For me it was usually a side salad with my lunch or a salad before dinner, which happened to be when I took in about 50 percent of my calories, so eating a salad beforehand cut back on the amount of food I was eating. Because of that and the great nutrients you'll be getting, your body will slowly start to stop sending a constant barrage of hunger signals from your brain to your stomach. You will become less hungry and your food intake will voluntarily going down.

Step 5: Add fifteen minutes of walking three days out of the week.

The next step is to get some exercise. Once you're feeling better, like I was, it's time to get moving. I was certainly not up for the gym and I couldn't jog more than out to the mailbox, which hurt my knees, not to mention that it would make my heart feel like it was going to burst in my chest. That wasn't going to meet my criteria of being easy, so I decided to just walk. It was free, it didn't strain my body, it could be done anywhere, and it is about the most natural motion our bodies were designed to do. Try three days per week for fifteen minutes. It equates to a walk around the block.

Once you've been walking for a while, you may want to turn it up a notch. Keep walking three days per week but try increasing each walk to thirty minutes. Soon, you can push it up to forty-five minutes. Keep this in mind: during the first twenty minutes of exercise you are mostly burning off stored sugar, after thirty minutes you tap into more fat, and by the time you reach forty-five minutes you're burning mostly fat. I liked the sound of this. This was the kind of release that I needed, a physical release of fat.

I've found that a heart rate monitor with a watch and a chest strap helps to keep my heart rate at about 60-70 percent of my maximum. You can go to www.SixSimpleTruths.com to calculate your maximum and target heart rates more accurately, but a good guideline is:

Maximum Heart Rate (MHR) = 220 – your age

Target Heart Rate for Fat Release = MHR x .65

Eventually, you'll want to work up to a good pace and try to get a sweat going but for starters, all that is required is that you get moving. And remember, if you can't manage to get 15 minutes in all at one time, you can always get in 2 minutes here and 5 minutes there. It all adds up and steps are steps. I find myself getting exercise in while waiting for doctor's appointments, while waiting for my wife in the mall (and waiting, and waiting). The waiting place is an excellent place to get some walking in. Keep your eyes peeled for opportunities to walk and they will appear. You will soon find yourself upping the ante and walking much more regularly.

Step 6: Add another piece of fruit (two total) per day.
You'll probably be ready to add a second piece of fruit at this point. Here I suggest a more mindful strategy of timing when you eat your fruit. Place your first piece of consumption between breakfast and lunch and your second piece between lunch and dinner. This accomplished several things for me. It helped me cut down on all the unhealthy snacking, which I could still participate in any time I wanted to. It also kept my blood sugar at a constant and more even level. With your sugar levels more constant, you will be less prone to dramatic and sudden hunger pangs that cause you to binge or overeat. Also, as I've mentioned, we humans eat by volume, so two new pieces of fruit may have just displaced some doughnuts or cookies somewhere in your daily menu. Now you're getting some traction.

Step 7: Add another vegetable (two) per day.
If it works for the fruit, it has to work for vegetables, right? A very loose rule of thumb for adding veggies is to try to have

one with at least two of the three main meals per day. It doesn't always work out that way, but it's something to shoot for. Sometimes this can be accomplished by adding a healthy pile of lettuce and tomato to a sandwich. For me, it usually took the shape of turning my lunch, whatever it was going to be, into a salad of some sort. If I was eating out, I'd order a burger or a chicken sandwich and tell them to put it on top of a salad. At home, I usually bought the lettuce that was washed and bagged so that in the heat of the moment, when I was hungry, I could put a salad together very quickly. Perhaps you have more patience than I had; I just found this to work out better for me. Anytime I could make eating healthy more convenient with less to think about, I did it. If that meant I had to pay a little more for my lettuce, I was prepared to accept that. Besides, I was saving a fair amount of money from simply eating less junk.

Don't worry, if you're still hungry after you've eaten this, just wait at least five or ten minutes and you can eat something else. You'll probably find, however, as I did, that you won't want or need to eat anything else. Like my grandmother used to say, it's a case of your eyes being bigger than your stomach. Either way, it's comforting to know that you can still eat whatever you want, just eat the veggies first.

Step 8: Add green tea.
The next step was an easy one for me. Haven't they all been so far? Drink green tea. I started reading some articles on the benefits of green tea and even read an interesting book called *The Ultimate Tea Diet* by Mark Ukra (Dr. Tea). There are antioxidants and great things in green tea called catechins, which promote good health and can help control your hunger. Besides

all of that, I liked the taste of it. So I decided to throw two to three cups per day in the mix. I personally buy loose green tea, which is much less expensive and tastes better. I make eight to ten cups of it on the stove in a big pot, and when it's colder outside, I put some hot green tea in a thermos and bring it with me. When it's warmer, I turn the extra into iced tea by diluting it with one part water and one part tea and end up getting my tea and water requirements at the same time. My second fill up of water is just plain water.

I think part of the reason tea works is that it helps to nourish your soul. It's taking time to take care of you. For years I watched my wife go to bed every night with a cup of herbal tea. One day I finally got it. She was taking care of herself. This is one thing that we overweight people quite often won't or don't do. Take care of ourselves. This is evident by the physical manifestations of our bodies. It is interesting, though, how prevalent it is, from my point of observation, how deeply overweight people take care of others so well, so often, so genuinely and generously, and ask for nothing in return. We're a strong army of passionate and loving people who are temporarily stuck in these unintended bodies. It is my belief that if even a small percentage of us took better care of ourselves, the world would be vastly improved by our positive influence and our nurturing effects. So many beautiful gifts would be given to the world that are now stored away and hidden due to oppression from an unhealthy lifestyle. That is called "leveraging our efforts," and I'm committed to making it happen.

In any event, I usually stop drinking my green tea in the early afternoon, even though the caffeine levels are lower than regular black tea, because I don't want to take anything in that might disturb my sleep at night. You can look up online all of the good things you get out of green tea, but knowing why won't make it work any better. That, and healthy, thin people in China have been drinking this stuff for thousands of years and knowing it is good for them. That's proof enough for me...throw it on the pile and keep on truckin'. A lot of what I did was based more on intuition and a listening to my heart. I didn't always understand all the reasons why I was doing all the things I was doing. The wisdom was later shown to me when I did more research on the subjects. I am only asking you to trust your heart and then follow it. I can tell you it all really did work. I'm proof.

Step 9: Add a good night's sleep.
The next major revelation that came to me through my research was the value and importance of a good night's sleep. When I was at my heaviest, as I've mentioned, I had sleep apnea. I was not getting good sleep at all. That was one of the biggest obstacles I had to overcome. Getting adequate sleep is essential in allowing your body the rest it needs to repair and operate at ideal levels. I notice to this very day, even in my healthy state, that if I don't get enough sleep, my hunger is much stronger and I care less about my healthy decisions. On top of that my energy levels are much lower and my metabolism has come to a halt. If this means you have to go to bed earlier, then make the appropriate adjustments in your life to allow this to happen. Your health and ultimately your life are hanging in the balance. Nothing could be more important. Add a good sleep affirmation to your list and make sure to get enough rest. It should not be overlooked that alcohol can also directly affect your body's ability to sleep, as well as leave you feeling worn out and burnt up the next day.

Step 10: Add details to your food log.
By this time you may notice, as I did, that even though what you are doing is easy, there are definitely days where you aren't quite getting it all done and that you could have if you were just a little more mindful. Your food log does not have to be complex, but it is necessary in your transformation, especially for the long-term success you're after. To this very day, I promise you, I write down, every day, everything I eat and drink. Don't worry, it's not that bad. I've been doing this for years and I hardly notice anymore. I currently categorize this right up there with brushing my teeth. It's just what needs to be done. No big deal. It will become part of your everyday ritual if you just keep doing it.

You started in the second simple truth, awareness, by writing down what you are eating. Now you might find it helpful to write down what time you eat, how much, and how many calories it had. It isn't my intention to get in to a controversial and heated debate with anyone over whether or not we should have to write down our intake or track calories or not, but let me say this. If your goal was to retire at a reasonable age and have x amount of dollars in your savings to allow you to do this, would you track your spending habits and have a budget that you stick to every month, or would you just hope that by the time you retired the money would just be there?

Writing what and how much you eat is no different than tracking your money. Did you realize that the average obese person eats 50 percent more calories than they think they do? I'm not sure how we got to the point as a society where we have come to think we can close our eyes to the reality of a situation and then wonder why it is not improving. It's no wonder we're all confused as to why we're overweight and why losing weight seems like a hopeless endeavor. This all lies at the heart of the second simple truth, awareness.

One thing you can rely on is that *there is nothing wrong with your true nature*. You are perfect at your core. Your weight is a function of an energy balance or lack thereof, but if you can't look honestly at how much is coming in and how much is being expended, well, solving that imbalance is about as hopeful as solving a trillion-dollar deficit by refusing to look at how much we're spending. Like they say in Weight Watchers, you bite it, you write it.

And remember, your failures are your learning grounds. Every time in the past during my many failed attempts at controlling my weight that I stopped writing down what I was eating, the program would always end in failure within the next two weeks. I have countless food journals to back this up stored away in boxes. I saved them all because I was convinced one day I'd figure it out and they would come in handy somehow. Did they fail because I stopped writing or did I stop writing because the diets failed? I really don't know. Probably a little bit of both, but it is a powerful thing to become aware of. It really pays off big time.

Later, as I progressed, I became a little more sophisticated and started to track protein, carbohydrates, and fats. The ratio you need depends on your body, your activity, and your goals. We're all different, and as such we have different needs. For a sample diet log that I use, go to www.SixSimpleTruths. com. You can also figure out how many calories you need in a day to release body fat by calculating your Basal Metabolic Rate (BMR), which is also available on the Web site. All the information and tools you need to accomplish all of this can be found on my Web site, for free.

Remember, there are 3500 calories in a pound of pure fat. As I progressed, my strategy for steady and effective fat release became a 500-calorie per day deficit on my calorie intake and to burn an extra 500 calories with my activity levels. This averaged a 7000-calorie deficit per week. Divide that by 3500 calories in a pound of fat, and I averaged a two-pound release every week. It's really very simple math.

Keep in mind that this is averaged over time. Your week-to-week results can and will quite often look very different than this. It is noteworthy that I was months into my journey before I even remotely wanted to track my consumption this closely. Do not feel you need to rush into this aspect; if you feel resistance to anything presented here, don't do it until you can release that resistance. You will know when you are ready. Go back to the release techniques and start to let the resistance go. When you are ready to progress to the next step, you will be ready and it will not be a fight.

Throughout this entire process, I never felt like what I was doing I couldn't keep doing for the rest of my life. This is the key to permanent fat release: sustainability. That was something I never had with a crash diet or a super intense workout program. They just weren't things I was prepared to do for the rest of my life. This is an important concept. As we've talked about, if you want to have the result, you have to start by BEING the person who would naturally and effortlessly have those results. You then DO the things that person would do. If you have no intention of doing these things for the rest of your life, then the results you do achieve will not be permanent, or you will not HAVE them for very long.

We get so caught up in wanting to have the physical results

and the transformed body and then say "OK, what do I have to DO to get that body because I know that once I HAVE it I will be in a different place, I will BE happy." Just like the lottery, it doesn't work that way. Statistically speaking, these results are worse than lottery winner results, with a shocking 95 percent of people ending up in "physical bankruptcy." You can start to think like a thin and healthy person right now, and your physical body will follow suit every time.

Are you having fun yet? Do you like the concept of adding? Have you noticed nothing has been taken away from you? That's not to say you haven't released some negative or undesired habits, but if you did it was by your own choosing, right? This is very empowering. You see, it's not some health expert telling you to eat this or that and do this workout program or that one, or you will fail. It's you designing and intending your own health on your own terms. It's you following what comes naturally, because when you can release the unneeded things, what's natural is what's right. It works because you have freedom to do what you want to do at any moment you like.

I have news for you. Even on a diet, this is true. You can always do whatever you want. It's called free will. You might as well embrace it and work with it rather than try to fight against it. This is all part of allowing yourself to find your own path. There are as many ways to release weight as there are people who want to release it. Everyone is going to do it a little differently. It's no wonder there are thousands of diets out there. I'm just trying to "boil the fat" off and show you some common denominators of what does work, some simple basic truths that you can always depend on.

SIX SIMPLE TRUTHS

• • • • • •

"*The truth is incontrovertible, malice may attack it, ignorance may deride it, but in the end; there it is.*" — *Winston Churchill*

• • • • • •

HEALTHY LIVING

I WOULD LIKE to introduce you to a beautifully simplistic and easy-to-use form. I call it my healthy living checklist, and I'm not sure where I'd be without it. This is a sure-fire way to help keep you on track. You can download this great tool on my Web site at www.SixSimpleTruths.com.

I didn't have the checklist in the beginning, and while I made it anyway, I certainly got knocked around my fair share as I fumbled through the dark and tried to make it out into the light. When I finally arrived at the end, I had developed many useful tools and methods of getting from here there with effortless ease. You, my beloved and empowered reader, do not have to fumble through the dark like I did. You can think of this checklist like a flashlight in a pitch-black room. It's free, it's been proven to work, and it's all yours.

What happens all too often is that when we have failed in the past at diets, work, even relationships, it's because we started to forget the little things. This is a slippery slope that can be difficult to recover from because all of the little things make a big thing. This checklist makes sure you've got your basics covered. Ask any pilot about a checklist and they'll tell you they go over one every time they fly. Why? Because, in their line of work, failure is not an option.

Well, when I started my journey, failure was just not an option for me either, and it doesn't have to be one for you. You have too much value to give to the world and too much joy and passion to experience and spread to be stuck in this vicious cycle of self-destructive behaviors and miserable experiences that frustrate you to no end. So print out the checklist and use it daily. I keep all mine in a three-ring binder. Every night I get out a little green highlighter and fill in the box if I've done the thing according to plan. I fill in the number of steps I've taken, and so on. It takes only a couple of minutes each night to prepare for a lifetime of joy and success.

This is easy and it actually becomes fun. You can go back and look at your results and your weight, which helps you track your progress and become aware of what is working for you. You'll see there's a place at the bottom for notes or comments. Maybe you came up with a great idea or there is something you want to experience or something you want to try to work on or a book you want to read; or perhaps you think of someone you want to call and encourage. Capture it. My father always called this "harpooning an idea."

You have too many great thoughts to just let them get away. There will be many great ideas that will come to you while you are working on this chart. You will be very connected to your true nature, or your inner being, from which your creativity flows. Allow these great ideas to come to you and allow yourself to capture these ideas and thoughts. This will expand your horizons and create a new and better life experience for you.

This process of allowing has been incredibly powerful for

www.SixSimpleTruths.com

Checklist for Healthy Living

	M	T	W	Th	F	Sa	Sn	Date __/__/__ through __/__/__	Net cals
daily	☐	☐	☐	☐	☐	☐	☐	Calories within range (BMR to BMR -500)	
calories eaten - BMR									
daily	☐	☐	☐	☐	☐	☐	☐	10,000 steps/day	
steps								Put # of steps in previous blocks from pedometer	
	☐	☐	☐	☐	☐	☐	☐	Any additional exercise (yard work, labor, etc.)	
extra calories burned									
daily	☐	☐	☐	☐	☐	☐	☐	Mirror work (abundance, love appreciation)	
daily	☐	☐	☐	☐	☐	☐	☐	Meditation (5 minutes minimum)	
daily	☐	☐	☐	☐	☐	☐	☐	Affirmations and visualizations	
daily	☐	☐	☐	☐	☐	☐	☐	Review goals	
daily	☐	☐	☐	☐	☐	☐	☐	Vegetables (minimum 2 servings/day)	
daily	☐	☐	☐	☐	☐	☐	☐	Fruits (minimum 2 servings/day)	
daily	☐	☐	☐	☐	☐	☐	☐	Write down complete food logo	
daily	☐	☐	☐	☐	☐	☐	☐	6-8 cups filtered water	
daily	☐	☐	☐	☐	☐	☐	☐	7-8 full hours of sleep per day	
daily	☐	☐	☐	☐	☐	☐	☐	Vitamins/EFAs	
daily	☐	☐	☐	☐	☐	☐	☐	No eating within 2 hours of bedtime (exception: fruit and vegetables)	
daily	☐	☐	☐	☐	☐	☐	☐	Green tea (2-3 cups/day)	
daily	☐	☐	☐	☐	☐	☐	☐	Protein (several servings of quality protein)	
3x/wk	☐	☐	☐	☐	☐	☐	☐	Calcium (3 servings/week minimum)	

Total/3500 = projected change

previous weight _____ lbs / current weight _____ lbs

projected change _____ lbs / actual change _____ lbs

Affirmation of the week:

Notes/goals for this week:

me and can hit me at any time throughout my day. I've purchased a small digital recorder to capture my ideas, and later I make sure I take appropriate action by putting them on my goals list or turning them into an affirmation or putting them on my to do list. This is a key part of the process, and that is why I've put a section in the back of this book called "harpooning your ideas" where you can do this.

As you look at your checklist, you will see some new things in there, like not eating two hours before you go to bed. This is one of the last things I added because I didn't want to be too restrictive in the beginning. I found out through my food log that I was eating over half my daily calories after dinner but before bedtime! I knew enough about nutrition to know that this is one of the worst times to allow food to just sit in your guts. It has much higher probability of being stored as fat instead of utilized, and I found as I became aware that I felt worse in the morning after eating a lot late at night.

This sets off a complete chain of events that you don't want to happen. First, you just aren't that hungry for breakfast. Why is it bad to skip breakfast? The most important reason, from my perspective of achieving permanent weight loss, has to do with hunger control and metabolism.

Skipping breakfast, or any meal, is going to not only slow your metabolism but also increase your hunger for your next meal, which in this case would be lunch. Most of us speed through lunch if we even make time for a decent one, which then brings us to dinner, and are we incredibly hungry by the time it rolls around! This is where many people consume the bulk of their calories. There were certainly emotional reasons why I was eating so much, but there were physical reasons, too. Mainly that I had not taken in enough food throughout the day.

Here's the thing. If you want to eat right and keep your food intake at a reasonable level so that you can have a balance of energy with a slight deficit in order to release excess body fat, at some point you're going to have to control your hunger. I don't think most thin people truly understand what it means to be as hungry as an overweight person can get. The good news is you can change that. If you can get hunger to just say away in the first place, you won't have to tangle with it and it will be a nonissue. Do you see that this is how we've dealt with the majority of the issues thus far? As they've come up, we just flowed around the problems like water.

Hunger was something I used to be afraid of. I looked at it as the enemy and was always waiting for it to jump out and get me just when I was making good progress. Well, that was one of the concepts I had to release. I was attracting to me exactly what I was afraid of because I was focusing on what I didn't want.

Let me give you some sound, solid, and practical tools for handling hunger. First, let's cover the basics. Your hunger is stimulated when you haven't had enough to eat recently, right? The longer you go without eating, the hungrier you potentially get. Well, you're also messing with your blood sugar levels, and other chemical reactions are going on in your body, all of which are discussed in a very good book by Dr. Oz, *You on a Diet*. He puts things in a way that will make a lot of sense if you feel you need a deeper understanding of the inner workings of your body in conjunction with losing weight.

Underline this in your mind, highlight it, put it in bold, and repeat it to yourself over and over.

THERE IS NEVER A GOOD REASON TO BE HUNGRY!

You should never have to feel strong hunger like you may be accustomed to on a diet. If you ever are ever truly physically hungry, you should eat. I always did and still do allow myself to eat as many fruits or vegetables as my body wants. You always have that at your disposal. But the main way to eliminate ravenous hunger very quickly is to never skip a meal and to be sure you are eating enough at each meal. Feed your body breakfast, lunch, and dinner and definitely don't skimp on the first two.

I know the logic: "Well, I'm just not that hungry and if I'm not that hungry, I might as well just eat very light or maybe not at all. I mean, I ate enough food last night and look at me. I could stand to skip a meal." Do not. Don't ever skip a meal. This is a must. It's a new habit you will have to learn to develop or this will potentially remain a fight for you for the rest of your life. It's that important. Don't skip meals, and keep your meals all about the same size, tapering down with dinner if you feel like it, but not at the expense of loading back up before you go to bed.

The next hunger-management tool is to be sure not to leave your house without your water and some healthy food options like fruit and vegetables. One of the places I've identified that we most commonly fail in life is not due to a lack of willpower or knowledge. It's lack of preparation. Quite often, if we were better prepared in life, we would naturally and voluntarily make better choices, if only they were conveniently presented to us when we were feeling the hunger. So be aware, take your water bottle with you, and eat before you're starving. When you do feel hungry, that should also be a cue to have a drink of water, and if it's not mealtime, to eat your fruit and then just wait for a couple of minutes to give the hunger a chance to go away. Fruit and veggies are what you can and should be eating between meals. Bring as much as it takes to satisfy you. You will quickly get to the point where one piece will be plenty. Nature has a way of packaging things just right for us. I, personally, found apples to work well as they are filling, taste good, and are very portable.

Also, don't wait until you're absolutely ravenous to eat your snack. As a general rule of thumb, try not to go much longer than three hours without eating something. It was beyond that time that I would notice my hunger would grow to the highest levels. Controlling your hunger is much like controlling pain. You have to stay ahead of the pain. If you wait until it's throbbing to take the medicine, you're going to be in a lot of unnecessary discomfort. Well, the same principle applies here. If you wait until the hunger gets too strong, even the strongest of wills or determination can easily be steamrolled by your body's very strong hunger mechanism. This mechanism is an integral part of you and keeps you alive. It's the reason that we, as a race, have survived as long as we have.

In fact, the same is true for our incredible ability to store fat as efficiently as we do. There's nothing wrong with you that you can store fat so well. It's your body doing what it was designed to do for a very long time. It's just that this day and age, in our culture, most of us don't face the same challenges our ancestors did. They often had to go long periods of time with no food. To store fat was the body's only defense to keep it alive. And when they skipped meals, their body's metabolism would naturally slow down. This was a good thing. It was their body's wisdom saying, "We haven't been given any food lately,

so we'd better conserve what we have." And when your metabolism slows down, your energy levels naturally will follow
(burn more calories, have more energy; burn less, have less).

Now here's where the problem comes in. We're not starving
in this day and age. We may be starving for good nutrition,
but not for calories. We have access to a nearly endless and
abundant supply of food, most of which is devoid of real nutrients. Some people call them empty calories. This is the perfect
formula for putting on fat very quickly and feeling tired all the
time, all the while starving your body of the very things it truly
needs: vitamins, minerals, phytonutrients found in fruits and
vegetables, and quality protein, creating more hunger as your
body tries to get what it needs.

So don't play this game. Remember, nowhere have I told you
that you can't eat anything else; just be sure to eat all of your
meals and snack in between with fruit. Keep your water intake
high, and if you're still experiencing strong hunger, do one of
the release techniques I've described. Just know you always have
options other than overeating, and you don't have to feel hungry. This should empower you.

Supplements

Another powerful strategy is adding a protein shake to your
daily food intake. I've made a conscious effort to avoid telling
you exactly what to eat, but I would be missing an opportunity
to add incredible value if I left this out. Many of us, though we
take in more than our fair share of calories, tend to overlook
quality protein.

Protein helps you in a number of ways. It helps you control
hunger. It gives your body the building blocks it needs to re-

pair muscle tissue to keep a healthy, lean body mass. This in turn burns more calories and gives you more energy. If you ultimately end up adding more intensive exercise to your routine, taking in enough quality protein will become even more indispensible to you.

A Harvard study presented at the 2003 North American Association for the Study of Obesity demonstrated that people who over a ten-year period added two nutrition shakes per day to their diet were an average of 32.6 pounds lighter than the control group. Many of the test subjects did far greater than that. This clearly shows a long-term result, our goal with permanent fat release.

Shakes are an easy and delicious way to add good quality nutrition to your food intake. In a blender I mix whey protein powder with either water, milk, soymilk, or almond milk, to which I usually add frozen blueberries (an excellent antioxidant) and a little ice. I do this most every morning, at which time I am also reminded to take my vitamins.

Entire volumes could be filled on which vitamins to take, but after extensive research and speaking with my nutritionist, I take vitamins C, D3, E, a multivitamin, and most importantly essential fatty acids (EFAs) in the form of fish oil (either capsules or liquid). You may wish to extend your minerals and vitamins from here, but I implore you not to leave out the EFAs. You will start to feel immediate results, as they are "essential" to you releasing body fat.

Smile

That's right, just smile. Force one out if you have to. Right now, try it. Now, doesn't that feel good? Easy, right?

Smiling is also something that I started doing while I was exercising. I had always noticed so many people with these awful looks on their faces like they were eating lemons. Judging by nothing other than this, it's no wonder they struggle to keep on doing this. It's no wonder it becomes a challenge to keep this activity up day in and day out.

Probably most folks are not aware of this look on their face, or perhaps it's never occurred to them that they can choose a different look. Smiling can do a lot for you, including but not limited to releasing endorphins that just plain make you feel good; and like I said, that is really at the root of all of the things you want in life. It has a way of making your exercise much more enjoyable. It has a way of making your *life* more enjoyable, so there is simply no good reason not to do it more often. Smiling can make your hunger go away and it can make you feel good in an instant, but what's even more powerful is it makes everyone around you feel good as well, which brings us back around to the fifth simple truth, giving back.

It is for this reason that I have founded a nonprofit organization called mPower the World Foundation. Its major mission is to reduce the rate of obesity and promote good health in children. If we can direct our effort and attention on promoting good health in children, especially between the ages of three and five, inside of a single generation, I believe we can eradicate childhood obesity.

The Dalai Lama has said that if we could get every five-year-old to contemplate peace for fifteen minutes per day, we could eliminate war inside of one generation. I know the same could happen with childhood obesity, but we have to believe it can happen and stay focused on the positive outcome. It is my knowing that this foundation, along with the help of good people like you, will make this dream a reality.

A portion of all proceeds from this book and every other product or service I provide goes directly to this nonprofit organization to benefit this cause. If you or someone you know would like to contribute or get more involved, please go to www.SixSimpleTruths.com and click on mPower the World to read more about our mission. If we can instill good, quality habits in children so they are equipped to make good and healthy choices, then they will teach their children the same thing, and we can all leave a legacy of good health that can prevail from this moment forward. It is a beautiful thing to be a part of.

SIX SIMPLE TRUTHS

● ● ● ● ● ●

Dealing with Challenges

*"Come, come, whoever you are. Wanderer, worshipper, lover
of leaving. It doesn't matter. Ours is not a caravan of despair.
Come, even if you have broken your vow a hundred times.
Come, yet again, come, come." — Rumi*

I am often asked about how to carry on after making some
mistakes. I know that mistakes in past health programs I tried
were always what led me to stopping or failure. I would inevitably mess up somewhere along the way. I now realize that I
was attracting the failure. I was creating a game with a set of
rules that would eventually cause me to lose. It was almost
guaranteed. No one I know can run off pure motivation and
determination for their entire lives, but the rules of the game I
had created in the past required a near perfect record in order
to stay in control and "win" the game.

You know, it always amazes me how overweight people can
so easily take a setback and turn it into a reason to fail. In very
few other important areas of our lives do we take such a position. What would you do if you made a mistake with one of
your children? Would you just say, "Oh well, I messed up. I

guess you're on your own now because I'm not fit to do this job"? Or if you made a mistake at work, would you say to your boss, "Sorry, boss, I just filed that paperwork completely incorrectly and I really don't deserve to be here any longer. I'm sure you'll find a great replacement. Good luck"? What if a baseball player quit every time he made a mistake? Most of the time up to bat they don't even hit the ball. Of course, we can see in these situations that so-called "failure" is just a part of life; it's probably going to happen at some point. It's OK. You can still succeed at this and make some mistakes. Take heart. This trip is supposed to be fun. Just get up and keep going and don't take yourself too seriously.

There were still times when I would feel depressed or just plain unmotivated as I went through this process. I want you to know that it's OK to feel this way. Please don't be too hard on yourself. This is natural and normal. You probably developed habits over the course of a lifetime that you are now letting go of, which can be uncomfortable for your body and your ego. You may be letting go of some of your identity as an overweight person and feeling a little fear about that.

This can be a huge momentum booster for you if you can recognize that your ego has masterfully developed an entire program to keep you the way you are, as we discussed under the third simple truth, release. If you have been on this path and following the guidelines and suggestions here and you are experiencing some unusual feelings of depression or anger, or any unexplained resistance, or you find yourself slipping and making mistakes when things were going so well, you will know that you are close, my friend. You are probably closer than you have ever been before.

This is your clever ego's way of making one last attempt to

sidetrack you, to throw a stick in your spokes and mess you up. It desperately tries to get you to stop. You see, in a way you caught your ego asleep at the wheel. Your changes have been so gradual in nature that it didn't really take notice. It ignores you for a while until it realizes that progress is being made. Then it frantically grabs everything it has in the emotional toolbox and throws it all at you at the same time to get you to stop. You are jeopardizing your ego's existence. Remember, it's trying to keep you safe, but your heart has much more strength than your ego or your physical body will ever know. It is your connection to source energy and is therefore endlessly abundant in strength and energy.

You can rejoice when you reach this point in your transformation because you are past the halfway point, at the peak of the hill, so to speak, and it only gets easier from here. So, if you're experiencing these feelings, congratulations! Keep going. You're getting so close, perhaps closer than you've ever been. You're doing great.

Unexpected Adversity

I'd like to pick back up with my story. I'd been doing everything that I've recommended to you so far, and I was gaining some momentum. I felt better than just good. I felt strong and energetic, much stronger than I had in a long time. I don't mean strong like I could lift up a car, I mean strong like I could maybe keep going here. Like the kind of mental fortitude I had previously thought was nothing but a distant memory for me. The kind of strength that lies in your heart and gives you the capacity to keep on going regardless of what lies in your path. This felt good.

It was about this time in my life that I was hit with some pretty devastating news. My father, business partner, and dear friend was diagnosed with a serious form of cancer. The doctor suggested that he had six to twelve months to live. I'll never forget the way my heart dropped. This was much bigger than the kind of thing that would have spun me backward and taken me down in the past, but by this time, I had gained enough strength in my heart to keep moving forward. I remember mornings on the treadmill at the gym where I would just lose it and break down, but *I just kept walking*. It was all I could do.

I learned to see through my father's physical illness and not focus on his failing body but rather his loving soul, which was very much alive. No matter what our bodies go through, our true nature, our soul, is still alive and can always be honored and celebrated. I love my father very much, and neither my transformation nor my personal growth—and therefore this book—would have been possible at the speed and timing it occurred without the countless talks we had and his endless support and encouragement. I still feel your love, Dad.

This was a very special but difficult time, and I suppose walking became a metaphor for me. It helped me deal with the stress in a positive way. It helped me be strong for my family and be there for my father, instead of being in some other awful place in my life, numbed out with food and alcohol. I knew inherently that I needed to be present now and feel what was happening. I had to experience this or I would later look back and regret it.

I bring this up to you, my beloved readers, to let you know that if adversity should strike while you are transforming, please know that you can keep going, that it is actually easier to go through the pain than it is to hide from it. Exercise, even just walking, is a very effective and incredible release to help you cope with the stress. Every single event in your life will pass, including your physical presence on this earth and the hardships you face. It is a part of the human experience. I believe firmly that my state of gratitude and my physical state of well-being was awakened by decent nutrition and hydration. Even if I was only partially transformed, this helped me work through this stage of my life. I learned to be truly grateful for what and who I have in my life. I learned that there is no time for negative thoughts or dwelling on what is not working. Furthermore, I learned that dwelling on such things just attracts more of the same to us. For now, make no mistake about it, exercise is a physical form of release, and it will help you deal with stress in a positive way.

Three Negative Affirmations

I do want you to be aware of what's going on in your mind and in your body and what you've probably been feeling at the end of a failed diet. I always ended up feeling the same way at the end. What a failure I am. Why can't I lose weight? What is wrong with me?

STOP! Hit the pause button and play that back.

1. What a failure I am.
2. Why can't I lose weight?
3. What is wrong with me?

Have you ever felt that way? If you've been on this roller coaster ride before, you most likely have. Maybe you have some even more choice words, accusations, or other ways of beating yourself up even worse. But stop and look at what you've just told and asked yourself. First you affirmed the very thing you didn't want. This is something, the dark side of affirmations that some people just don't see.

In the past, right here is where you would have lost me to a twelve-pack of beer and a double order of chicken wings, drums, hot, extra crispy, with blue cheese—and while I'm at it, throw in the fries, too. I would have woken up the next day feeling awful; I would have been useless and eaten whatever because I really just didn't care. And I'm not going to tell you that didn't happen on my journey. It did happen, more than a couple of times. Though I was feeling much stronger than I had in a long time, these old feelings would resurface and come back to haunt me. I needed to do something easy, simple, something that would recharge my inner strength because when you hit a moment of weakness like that, your strength feels so low. It was at one of those points that I felt like I wanted to turn back and quit. I had come so far, and I didn't think I could bear the pain of another failure.

"I'm not perfect, you know. Sometimes I fall down. The important thing is I get right back up." —Ozzy Osbourne

It was right at that point that I asked for help. I'd never really done that in the past when it came to my weight. I closed my eyes and in a moment of desperation asked for some guidance. What was I doing wrong?

Help came. It was in the form of a book that I pulled out of a box of books that my father had given me, *Creative Visualization* by Shakti Gawain. I started to read through the pages and saw a ray of light. Affirmations and visualization were what was missing in my effortless ease program here. By now hopefully you've been saying your affirmations regularly for a while. Whenever you're discouraged, it's a great time to review what you've been affirming.

Underline this in your mind.

**You can and do affirm things every day,
and it works, every day.**

This isn't hocus pocus positive thinking nonsense that some people write affirmations off to be (I used to be one of those people). It is very real, and until you realize or become aware of how real it is, you'll be doing damage and not even knowing why. You'll be thinking there is something wrong with you or wrong with the world. But everything is the way it should be. There are rules and laws out there. Learn them and it all becomes very easy.

Imagine if I sat you down to a chess table and told you to start playing someone who was very good, even though you only understood a couple of the rules of the game. Very quickly, they would beat you and take all your pieces away and you would be left feeling battered and defeated. No fun. Now imagine that you keep coming back to play that same chess game over and over, never taking the time to learn the rules, and continue to get beat, badly, every time. You wouldn't want to play anymore. You would probably give up. Welcome to the 95 percent of people who fail at diets. Most of the five percent who succeed have stubbornly hung on so long that they actually, inadvertently have learned the rules.

This is exactly how we get with weight loss. We feel so beat up and tortured that we don't even want to play anymore.

Consider this book an easy how-to guide to understanding and applying the rules. Get some of the basics, and winning is not that difficult. When you truly grasp it, you'll understand that you're controlling both sides of the board and you can do anything you want to. You are your own opponent. You can make the game easy or hard. When you understand this, it becomes, first of all, easy, and second of all, fun to accomplish anything you set your intention on.

Always remember Jack Canfield's first principle in his great book *Success Principles*: Take personal responsibility. Even if you still choose not to change your actions, you have to at least own them. These actions are yours and not anyone else's. If you've made the three negative affirmations above, you just affirmed that you are a failure. Please understand that this kind of self-talk will attract many more failures to your life. This is the worst kind of self-talk, the negative, destructive, beating-yourself-up kind of self-talk. Monitor this and be aware. What are you telling yourself? Because whatever it is, I can assure you that your reality will eventually look a lot like what you're describing in your mind.

"Why can't I lose weight?" is a question I have asked myself in the past hundreds of times. This isn't a question you can go anywhere but down with. It's a certain death toll for your "diet" but more importantly for your health (the diet can die, we won't be needing it). Think about that question. *Why can't I lose weight?*

Well, first of all, it's false because I can almost guarantee that at some point you have successfully lost weight, probably very recently if you're having this discussion with yourself. Secondly, you don't want to lose weight, you want to release it so that it will not have to return; therefore you're calling it by the wrong name. This is like calling your dog by saying, "Come on, Max" when his name is Jack, and then wondering why he's ignoring you. Don't be surprised if your neighbor's dog Max shows up.

Most importantly, this question prompts no solutions to the current challenge you're facing, and unless you desire to stay where you are at, this does not make any sense. You can learn to ask yourself more empowering questions, questions that can build you up, questions you can learn from, questions that can actually give you a chance of succeeding.

You wouldn't sit down to a poker table and play cards if you knew you could never win even one hand, would you? No, you can see that it makes no sense to play that game; nor does it to ask yourself questions like this one. All you have to do is become aware of the questions you ask yourself, and you will start making better selections because you do want to win at this game and get positive results. You don't want to feel this pain over and over again.

The last question, and this one really breaks my heart, is "What is wrong with me?" This is inevitably where I ended up with all of my diets in the end. "What is wrong with me? This was supposed to work. This was supposed to be the answer. I had such high hopes this time." Every time you try and fail at one of those diets or programs, your will is crushed a little more and your spirit is run over like a flattened squirrel on the freeway.

Please, please don't do this. Even if you fail, don't do this. I'd really rather see you do nothing at all than this self-imposed torture, and I'd much rather see you accept yourself the way you are and find a way to love yourself anyway. My friend, I can't say it enough: there is nothing wrong with you. You are perfect, whole, and complete. It's just that you aren't living in the body your true nature is aligned with. Align the two and you will pull away from it naturally, automatically, and effortlessly.

Revisiting Meditation

Stress, as I've talked about, was one of the biggest hunger triggers for me. What I found was that if I could spend fifteen to twenty minutes per day getting quiet and eliminating the mental rambling in my brain, releasing the random thoughts that entered my mind, I had a much easier time keeping stress out of my life.

Start with five minutes to begin with, more if you feel you have time. Consistency is going to be the key to your success, and small steps are fine as long as you take plenty of them. There is no need to be intimidated by the process of meditation. It isn't something only reserved for Buddhist monks in some monastery in Tibet; far from it. It is simply quieting your mind and letting the stress and discomfort flow out of your body. In this quiet state you will connect with your true nature, with your inner self, your heart. This connection is vital because it is in your true nature to be thin and healthy.

The more you can connect with this nature, the easier it will become for you to move into that reality. Meditation can also be a good time to simply contemplate a thin and healthy you. Always keep this image in your mind. Carry it with you everywhere you go. I actually cut out pictures of what my body was going to look like from a magazine and put them where I could see them every day.

Your meditation time can be a time to visit the future you, as well. Close your eyes and get quiet. Go somewhere you won't be disturbed. In your mind's eye, see yourself as your true nature is. Thin, happy, and healthy. Living the satisfied life you intend to live. You can approach your "self of the future" in a meditative state and ask yourself questions about how you got through different challenges, and you can give yourself guidance and love and support.

This may sound a little different from what you may be used to, but to get an example of what I'm talking about, download a quick, guided meditation for free on my Web site at www. SixSimpleTruths.com. There is also a written copy that you can read aloud and record for your own listening or have a friend read it to you. Just remember, meditation is a natural process. It is nothing more than quieting your mind and connecting with your heart. You don't have to be concerned with doing it wrong. It, like any skill, will become easier and more effective the more you do it.

You see, with the meditation techniques, the release techniques, regular walking, an increased awareness of your different states, and a little knowledge of how to effectively change your states, which is what you've now learned, you no longer have to feel trapped or feel like you're just a victim to the stress in your life.

I'll remind you, too, that stress does *not* exist in the world as a thing to watch out for or something that can attack you. You can't see it touch it or feel it. That is because you create it. It exists only in your mind because you allow it to. And it's important to know that you yourself are the magnificent creator of all the thoughts in your life and therefore experiences in your life—not only stress, but joy and happiness, too.

The way to experience more joy and less stress is to stay in a more relaxed state of mind more of the time. For me, this was about 90 percent of the solution to my fat release. It helped me to remain relaxed all the time when I realized that I controlled 100 percent of my thoughts, and my thoughts led me to feel one way or another. It really is simple when you can step back from it all. Even to this day, I know I can release the tension in my head, neck, shoulders, and mind in an instant and re-peat the words I learned from Dr. Wayne Dyer: "I want to feel good." Any time you want, that is available. The real key here is not just in the ability to release. We are all capable of doing this quite easily, as you will see. The real key is staying aware of your mental tension, and you will then watch your hunger dissipate with the stress. This is the antidote to emotional over-eating, and you can do it.

You will come to develop a strong connection with your true nature, your heart; and your life will reach another level of sat-isfaction and realization. The words you use and the thoughts you have will then be tied to your heart's wisdom, and you will find it easy to attract much more than just good health. You can attract anything you desire, and you will find your real desire is to be joyful.

Defining Success

I would be remiss if did not make you aware of some of the unintended reactions you could receive from others as a result your personal transformation. You see, not everyone in your life or that you may encounter will be 100-percent thrilled about the changes in you. Many of these people liked things just the way that they were, and you had to go and change things up. Remember, change is one of the leading causes of fear in most people. You may have stirred up that fear in them.

Please know that you are not responsible for anyone else's feelings and you have no control over anyone else's thoughts. You have to do what's right for you because that's all you have control over. Some may resist your actions or your thoughts. Some may have what seems like a much narrower view of the world. I know I used to. Some will say your thoughts and philosophies are ridiculous or try to belittle them in some way. To argue with such people only adds resistance to their emotions, thereby attracting more of the same resistance and even more pushback.

"You cannot speak of the ocean to a well frog." — *Chuang Tzu*

This does not mean they may not get out of their well one day, but it also doesn't mean that they are supposed to get out of their well. If anything, it will only be love and acceptance that will bring them out into the light, not fear. Some people aren't as ready as you are now. That is OK. It's a larger part of allowing. The beautiful and expansive forces of creativity that exist in and around us wouldn't be as powerful if everyone thought the same way.

Besides, there are literally millions of people who are just begging for help. Help them. You never need to look far for a soul in need of love. The people who are ready and willing will come to you.

Remember that some people aren't as easy to reach as others. You don't want to try to force feed your new ideas on anyone who isn't ready for them. You'll be doing yourself and them a much bigger disservice than you may realize. So as I've said before, learn to allow these people their thoughts and flow around them. The creek does not stop its flow because of one stone in the middle, no matter how big that stone may be. Be the water, not the stone.

It may help to realize that everyone is at a different place in their journey through life and has different experiences to draw on for evidence of their beliefs. We can learn from everyone, as everyone has something to teach. Stay humble, even through your successes, and you will be more apt to learn the lessons.

You have special gifts. You have special talents. You may not know yet exactly what they are. You may need to search your heart to find them, but know for certain that they are there. You have a special way of reaching people that no one else can. You have a special story that no one else can tell. You have music in your heart that must get out. You may be a brilliant artist or a strong communicator or a writer or perhaps you have a gift with children. Maybe you have the give of making people laugh or entertaining them in some way. Perhaps your gift is as a teacher, or perhaps you are gifted at helping people heal. It takes all of us together; we need you here on this earth.

You do have a passionate calling. I know it was hard for me to see my gifts while I was buried under my insulation of excess weight. The answers all lie within your heart. There are people who can help you find this calling. There are some wonderful resources at www.SixSimpleTruths.com, under Resources, to help you find your passion in ways that are simple, easy, and clear, just like everything you've learned here.

You see, you set the boundaries in your life and you define what success is and what failure is, just like you define what a good day is and what a bad day is. There are some people out there who define a good day as a day above ground. Now, those are easy boundaries to succeed within! Unfortunately, many of us define success as something much harder to attain than that. The unfortunate thing is, many people who would be considered a success by most people's standards don't even consider themselves a success.

Everything you're going to go through on your journey will be necessary to get you to where you are going. Nothing is a mistake; it's just you learning and living your life the best you can with what you've got at the moment. If you take action that moves you farther away from that which you desire, then simply choose to learn from that and create a different experience next time. Keep your thoughts on that which you desire and realize that every part of your life's journey was necessary to get you where you are and therefore is necessary to get you to where you are going.

Your daily mirror exercises will help you out here. You have far more strength than you may realize, and you can tap it at anytime you'd like. Remember, it's all good and right and perfect. You only have failed when you have indefinitely stopped trying. If you are reading these words, you do not fall into this category.

Please believe me, I know a thing or two about being hard on yourself. I've been there for years on end, calling myself awful names and wondering what was wrong with me. No more. Whenever I seemingly backtrack, I just take notice of what happened, acknowledge it, and tell myself, "You're doing fine. You've come such a long way and I'm proud of you. This was just a slight deviation from the plan. Learn the lesson and keep going."

All of your so-called "mistakes" are your greatest lessons, which you will then be able to share with someone else to give them strength. I suppose what I'm saying is this: don't give your negative actions that much power because they will create more negative thoughts and then attract more negative actions, which ultimately will attract the undesired result you will have created. Your daily affirmations and visualizations will be a great help in this area. They will remind you every day of what you do want and help keep you mindful of what you desire.

"And you will know the truth, and the truth will make you free." — *John 8:32*

SIX SIMPLE TRUTHS

• • • • • •

EXPANSION

"There must be expansion in order for there to continue to be existence." — Esther Hicks

THE ENTIRE UNIVERSE is expanding in every moment. To exist in a state of stagnation is counterintuitive to our true nature. To expand and grow is the reason we are here—to learn and expand our boundaries from where we currently are to where we want to be.

No species can survive without constantly adapting to its environment and making itself better suited to it. This concept was something that I learned very late in my transformation, but I'm thankful I learned it at all. You see, many of the obstacles you may have to overcome will require information or expertise you may not yet have. This is OK. As you've already learned, everything you need to get where you're going is trying to get to you. You need only to allow it to come to you.

"As to methods there may be a million and then some, but principles are few. The man who grasps principles can successfully select his own methods. The man who tries methods, ignoring principles, is sure to have trouble." — Ralph Waldo Emerson

When we learn to live in a constant state of gratitude for everything we have, it becomes the next logical step to learn to take care of the only body we have to walk around this planet with. Many people may have special considerations that need to be addressed such as diabetes, heart disease, cancer, or any number of other dis-eases that are currently stopping them from living the life they were intended to live. These different situations may require different actions to overcome them, all of which could never be covered here inside these pages. But do realize that they can be overcome. In some cases it may mean medical intervention, medication, or different types of therapy. In many cases, you can heal yourself. There are two brilliant books, *Heal Your Body* and *You Can Heal Your Life*, written by the amazingly wonderful Louise Hay. If you are currently in a body that is in dis-ease, please start with these books and realize there is always hope to live an even better life. And this is from a woman who didn't start fully living her potential until what most would consider much later in life.

Learning about your body is just one aspect. Your desires in life are there for you to listen to and act upon. Somehow, we have arrived at a place in time where it is often frowned upon as selfish to follow your desires and act upon what you want. I've found that those who frown upon your desires are usually just upset with themselves for not following theirs. They need the most help. This is your life, not theirs, and you do not have to answer to them.

It is my knowing that the reason we are here on this planet is to act upon our desires. It is to make our lives more enjoyable and to enhance the experiences of those who are fortunate enough to be around us. It is to be constantly improving the circumstances of our lives, that we may enjoy the gift of life we have been handed more fully. Embrace your desires and live them. Dream as big as you can. If someone else has done the very things you want to do (and someone usually has), then you can as well. And even if no one else has done it, well, there are books full of examples of people who were the first to do things that others said were impossible.

You can lead a life of abundance: abundance in health, wealth, happiness, and overall contentment. Follow the truths in this book, and you can accomplish all you desire. I urge you to do so. I feel it is your responsibility. This is what I call expansion, and it is going on all around us every day. As a race, we know more about ourselves and the world in which we live than we did even five minutes ago. You know more now than you did when you started this book. You have adapted in some way, even if only in thought and not yet in action. All creations are born twice, first in thought and then in the physical realm. This is the natural way of things that are alive. Life wants to grow, thrive, get better, move faster, and improve. This is the very beauty and essence of all living things. Get in the flow and embrace it.

The great motivator Tony Robbins calls this concept CANI, constant and never-ending improvement. This is what leads to ultimate fulfillment in not only ourselves but also others around us. This is the opposite of stagnation. Stagnation leads to death; growth leads to life. Stagnation is where I was when I was at my heaviest. I had stopped dreaming. I had stopped learning. I had stopped listening to my desires and that little voice in my head that at one time told me I could fly. There were two brothers in Kitty Hawk who never stopped listening to that voice.

SIX SIMPLE TRUTHS

· · · · · ·

We were very much connected to this voice, this true nature of ourselves when we were young children. Children don't know what can't be done. Unfortunately, we tell them. As we grow, people tell us to grow up, get real, and stop dreaming. Well, I guess you could say I'm encouraging you to do the opposite and return to your youthful attitude. Be unrealistic. Dream again. This is the true state of your inner being, and until you align with it, you will not feel at ease. If you misalign with it for too long and to a greater degree, you may even be experiencing dis-ease. Let all of that go and expand and grow. There is an exciting world of knowledge and fun experiences to be had. It is yours to seize and a necessary step of a self-actualized life. Learn to open your heart and follow where it sends you. Learn to trust this part of you. It is when we stop trusting this part of us that we are led astray. Your heart is like a perfect compass. It will never lead you wrong. Your heart wants you to learn and stretch and grow. It wants, more than anything else, for you to be happy and full of desires, always reaching out for more. It knows you deserve to be satisfied.

And now we have come full circle. You have learned the value of practicing and living in a state of gratitude and how that will open you up to receive all the good in your life the universe has to offer. You are now aware of the power of practicing mindful awareness in every aspect of your life, how only through this awareness can you really get connected to the world around you in the deepest possible way, and to the true nature of your heart.

From there you've learned to release negative, self-limiting beliefs and thoughts. The habits that weren't working for you any longer, the emotions that have keep you in fear—release them out to the universe where they can dissipate, as they serve you no longer and will bring you no closer to your desires.

You have learned to allow. To allow that space this release has created to be filled with nothing but pure love and good intention, to allow the great and wonderful people and information into your life, to allow the incredibly awesome events simply to unfold in front of you without having to control them or be afraid of them.

You've come to know that all of this will have true value and will work when you can learn to apply the knowledge you've learned, and that it doesn't have to be hard. In fact, nothing could be more natural and easy because that is your true nature and that of the universe. The universe never struggles to create anything. It all comes with effortless ease.

Finally, you've learned that to keep these great and wonderful gifts close to your heart you have to circulate them and give them away, as much and as often and as quickly as you are able. That is the key to holding them forever and enjoying your new life indefinitely and to deeper levels than you ever thought possible, without ever having to go back to a place of lack ever again.

Yes, you have come a long way in a short time, but that's the way the universe loves it—speed and passion put together. So now, it's time to bring my story to a close. It was and is my passionate calling to guide you across the unknown to this point. To let you know that I love you and the universe loves you; that you were, in fact, intended here and are desperately needed. Just look around you for proof. The world needs your help. My biggest desire is one of empowerment for you. For you to realize that you don't need anything from a diet or a program or anything external to you because you have always had everything you need right inside of you.

This is the beginning, not the end. Don't be afraid. I and countless others are with you. You have the strength of the universe within you. There's a great line in the movie *Hope Floats*:

"Beginnings are usually scary and endings sad but it's the middle that counts the most. Try to remember that when you are at a new beginning. Just give hope a chance to float up. And it will…"

That middle is this moment. The only one you'll ever have, the only one that will ever matter, the only one available to you to make a difference. You can do it. Together, all of us, we can do it. When we align our intentions together, our success is inevitable and no other outcome is possible.

Let your heart be your compass and your thoughts, the wind in your sails. May you sail into your true passion and experience pure joy in all that you do as you take your part in making this world an even more joyful and beautiful place, like only you can do.

With nothing but love in my heart to give,

EPILOGUE

MY DEAR FRIEND, please know that though the words on the pages of this book have come to a conclusion, our time does not have to end here. I will be with you every day on your journey, along with millions of other good and kind folks just like yourself. There is an incredible community of people all at different stages of transformation, all with unique and special gifts to give. Some you will help and some will be able to help you. You can use my Web site to find them, but please know, they are everywhere around you and you will see them with more and more frequency.

I would encourage you to take pictures of the incredible journey you are embarking on. These pictures have a powerful energy to them that will speak to others and help them see light where they thought only darkness existed. If it is your desire, I will post your pictures and, when possible, even your story for others to read to be encouraged by your strength and example. Your strength will be shared in many, many ways, and as you know, it will only come back to you in full measure.

You can also find ways to get involved with the mPower the World Foundation I've discussed, a nonprofit organization that focuses its intention on children and how to make their future brighter and healthier. Information is available at www. SixSimpleTruths.com if your heart moves you in that direction, now or later. Please know there are literally an infinite number of great ways to give your time, energy, or resources back to your communities, and I encourage you to follow the ones that vibrate on your frequency. That is where you belong, and that is where you will enjoy yourself the most and be doing the most good. That is your only job here in this physical body: to enjoy yourself and others. Just listen to and trust your heart. It always knows.

Thank you for joining me and stay in touch.

With love,

SPECIAL THANKS

THOUGH THERE ARE many people who helped make this journey possible for me so that I may share it with you, I would like to give a special thanks to the YMCA. This was a safe place for me to transform in. Most of my physical work took place there and I owe a debt of gratitude for all of the good people who work there and dedicate their lives to helping others in the community. They picked me up when I was down and brushed me off and helped me to keep going even when the worst of times were upon me. The YMCA is a place that I suggest everyone take a look at and consider. Like they say, "The YMCA is also a great place to look inside yourself." The energy and resources that are available to you at a very reasonable price are priceless and not to be underestimated.

Today's YMCAs serve thousands of U.S. communities, uniting 21 million children and adults of all ages, races, faiths, backgrounds, abilities and income levels. Our reach and impact can be seen in the millions of lives we touch every year. Across the nation, YMCAs are committed to helping:

- **Children and youth** deepen positive values, their commitment to service and their motivation to learn
- **Families** build stronger bonds, spend time together and become more engaged with their communities
- **Individuals** strengthen their spiritual, mental and physical well-being

At every stage of life, YMCAs are there to help children, families and individuals reach their full potential.

From the bottom of my heart, thank you.

SIX SIMPLE TRUTHS

• • • • • •

APPENDIX

Suggested Reading

Getting in the Gap, by Wayne Dyer. New York: Hay House Inc., 2003

Mindless Eating: Why We Eat More Than We Think, by Brian Wansink. New York: Bantam Dell, 2006

The Success Principles: How to Get from Where You Are to Where You Want to Be, by Jack Canfield. New York: HarperCollins, 2005

Creative Visualization: Using the Power of Your Imagination to Create What You Want in Your Life, by Shakti Gawain. Novato, CA, 2002

The Ultimate Tea Diet, by Mark Ukra. New York: HarperCollins, 2008

The Gabriel Method, by Jon Gabriel. New York: Atria Books, 2008

You on a Diet: The Owner's Manual for Waist Management, by Michael F. Roizen and Mehment C. Oz. New York, Free Press, 2006

You Can Heal Your Life, by Louise Hay. Carlsbad, CA, 1987

Online Resources

Be sure to visit www.sixsimpletruths.com for a regularly updated list of resources to help you with your transformation.

www.animoto.com
This is a great Web site where you can go to create your own vision videos. It is very user friendly and will create a high quality automated production.

www.sedona.com

This is where you can find the legendary Sedona Method and all related tools and support. The Sedona Method is an effective system of release which can be used for anything, including releasing weight.

www.bodyfattest.com

This is a great Web site to find a mobile body fat testing facility. They regularly visit gyms and health facilities. Your body fat percentage is a much more meaningful number to know than your weight or even your measurements, and underwater hydrostatic body fat testing is the gold standard to determine your accurate body fat. One used to have to find a university or special facility and pay big dollars to get tested, but now you can just go to a mobile facility and get "tanked" for fifty dollars. If you're going to get dialed into a number, this is the one to become aware of. I get tanked regularly several times a year. This is also very helpful if you've been working out or trying to put on muscle so that you can determine if what you've been doing has been effective and know whether or not you need to alter your plan. It's very easy, quick, and discreet.

• • • • • •

My Six Intentions

I, _____, am clearly setting my intention on how I choose to live my life from this day forward.

1. It is my intention to start every day in a spirit of gratitude for what I have.
2. It is my intention to carefully pay attention to my thoughts and emotions by taking deliberate action and reserving time to quiet my mind, daily.
3. It is my intention to let go of all thoughts that do not move me in the direction of my heart's desires.
4. It is my intention to allow all the good, right, and perfect people, things, and situations into my life experience.
5. It is my intention to circulate the good that I attract to my life.
6. It is my intention to diligently apply my heart's wisdom in my daily activities.

I understand that I am improving every day and that my love and acceptance of myself is unconditional and not dependent on my actions on any given day. I hold these intentions firm and send them out to the universe with love so that I may align my perfect health and life with my true nature.

Healthy Affirmations

Please note that these prerecorded affirmations can be down-loaded by going to www.SixSimpleTruths.com and looking under downloads. I highly recommend working toward the point of recording these with your own voice and saving them to a digital device that you can play them back on. They will be more effective with your own voice. These are powerful affir-mations. They work. Use them regularly and consistently and they will help keep you on track. Remember to use them not only when you're feeling down but especially when you're feel-ing up. That is when they will have the greatest impact. That is when you are in a state of highest expectation and when they will take deepest root in your mind. As you progress and grow and expand, please feel free to add your own affirmations on whatever subject you would like more help with. I used these exact affirmations with incredible results and I feel they are a great place to start.

Every day, all day, my body is moving toward its natural healthy state, even while I sleep.

My body releases excess weight with as little effort as the uni-verse requires growing grass. It is effortless and enjoyable. My body inherently knows how to do this. I allow it to be.

I assist and work with my body to help reach its natural healthy state. I feed my body the highest quality foods and healthy supplements. My diet is balanced and full of fruits and vegetables.

I eat small, healthy, frequent meals. I follow a healthy plan. I drink at least eight cups of water a day. I eat healthy carbohydrates and lean proteins. Vegetables and fruits are my favorite foods because they feed my body the vitamins and nutrients it craves.

I am mindful of what I put in my body.

I know there is a time and place to eat, and I eat to nourish my physical body. I choose not to eat mindlessly. I focus on my food and enjoy it as nature intended. I eat slowly, calmly, and intentionally. I chew all my food thoroughly and taste every bite noting the textures and flavors.

I avoid putting things in my body that are not good for it. I love myself and my body too much to harm it.

I am at my ideal body weight already, in my mind. My body is catching up with my mind more and more every day.

Exercise is a part of my normal daily routine much like brushing my teeth or showering. I would no sooner postpone my exercise as I would skip anything from my normal maintenance routine.

I value exercise very deeply because I value my health. I value my health because I love myself. I take care of myself. My body deserves to be taken care of.

Exercise is not something I do to simply achieve a result. I exercise because it is who I am. It is part of being a healthy person. I am healthy. Everything I do for my body is sustainable. This will always be a part of my life, and it makes me content and full inside.

I get immense pleasure from my exercise routines. I value the time I set aside for myself for exercise. I connect with my heart and achieve inner peace. This empowers me and makes me want to do more. The more I do, the better I feel, and on goes the upward spiral.

I enjoy all physical activity. It makes me stronger, healthier, and happier, so I am always looking for opportunities to be active.

Physical activity releases stress and calms my body. This better equips me for life.

I visualize myself at my perfect weight and health. I imagine the clothes I wear and the reflection in the mirror. I see a slim and fit person. I look good and I am satisfied. I am healthy.

I see myself wearing the clothes I desire. I have a nice profile. I am fit and flexible. I am quick and light. I am healthy and my health is sustainable. I have abundant energy to keep up with my day.

I believe I can do whatever it is I decide to do. I understand that life is full of choices. I know the right choices bring about the desired results. I am mindful at all times. I am one with my body. We are the same. I respect my body because I respect myself.

I enjoy working for my success. I am dedicated. I have resolve. I am steady. If I should fall, I get right back up and keep moving in the direction of progress.

I practice the art of allowing. I allow good things to come into my life and I circulate them. I know I cannot control everything. I don't need to. I have a relaxed control over my life. I have the courage to keep trying. I am getting better every day. I am here for a reason.

I am mindful of the words I use. I understand that the quality of my life largely depends on the quality of my communication, most importantly with myself.

I value education. I continue to expand my knowledge and keep an open mind toward my physical and mental health. I read new books every week to keep learning

I am a better person when I am strong and healthy. This makes me more available to those I love. This is fuel for my soul to strive for improvement. I understand that one leads through action more than with words. I am a source of strength for others and that is a good thing. I am a good example for family and friends. I inspire. I bring the best out in other people. People notice my great energy.

I understand the past does not equal the future. Every step I take takes me one step closer to the person I aspire to be. It takes me farther away from the unhealthy person in my past.

I refrain from communicating negatively with myself and others. I look for the positive in the world. Everyone and everything is a gift and an asset to everyone else. I can. I am. I do. I am always looking for opportunities to empower myself and those around me. Greatness follows in my wake.

Everything is perfect and right. I am ready to achieve my perfect health. It is my normal homeostasis. I believe my efforts are worthy and true. I envision my life in my perfect, healthy state. I take a deep breath and I feel good. My body is functioning well. I am healthy. I am full of energy. I am full of hope and I am ready to give my special gifts back to the world. I am here to make the world better. I am beautiful. I love me.

HARPOONING YOUR IDEAS

HARPOONING YOUR IDEAS